THE Amishland STORYTELLER

*"I finally agree with what's
been said: I was put here for
a reason. But it wasn't for you
Amish or the community, and
it wasn't even for the girls in
the school…
It was for me."*

Other Works

by Audra Coldiron

Galoop-a-Doodle

Dear Sydney

Karma Cooking 2012

Karma's Kitchen

An inspiring true story of heart, hope, and humor against the odds.

The Amishland STORYTELLER

Battling cancer with family, friends, and faith

by Audra Coldiron

Foreword

Shortly after the start of 2015, my storyteller father called me up to ask if I would "help" him write a book with all his Amish stories that he had collected over the years while working with the Old Order in and around the tiny township of Bart, PA in Lancaster County. Though I knew my "help" would mean me doing most of the work, I agreed. After all, it would make a nice Christmas present. At that point, no one knew how ill he was.

Days after he had his gallbladder removed in April, I recorded three hours of his tales as they came to him, only intending to transcribe them and have them printed into a booklet. It was going to be easy. However, life had other plans.

In May he was diagnosed with advanced stage four prostate cancer with the highest starting PSA that anyone—including his doctors—had ever heard of. The following pages recount the miraculous Spring and Summer of 2015 when he beat the odds, interwoven with his beloved Amish stories that are based on true stories that are sometimes based on other stories themselves (and sometimes very loosely).

In other words, nothing you read in here about any individual should be taken as fact, ***especially if you are an Amish bishop***. Names have been changed, some people have been combined, but the events that occurred as part of the timeline happened. Just… maybe not *exactly* as I've written.

For my father, Johnny Dale Coldiron

also known as:

John
J.D.
Dad
Granddad
Honey
Coach
The Roving Bishop

and now ...
The Amishland Storyteller

CHAPTER 1

May 14, 2015

"Please, Lord, don't let it be cancer." That was the last thing Johnny remembered thinking as they finally wheeled him into the operating room.

Patti watched from the doorway of the room where they had waited all day, the permanent furrow between her aged beauty queen brow deepening, as her husband of forty-three years rolled down the sterile hallway on a stretcher, pushed along by nurses in scrubs and face masks. There she stood in suspended animation, holding his things close, short of breath, her gray-blonde shoulder length hair slightly disheveled. The farther away he got, the more lost she looked, until he disappeared out of sight.

In a few hours, the Coldirons would know exactly what those spots on his lungs were that had been discovered a few days before. "It could be anything from dust particles to scars," speculated the doctor who had ordered the biopsy.

They hoped to God this test would give them answers. Patti hoped they'd know, once and for all, why he had lost forty pounds and couldn't lie down to sleep; Johnny hoped this would be the last in a series of tests, all of which had been unsuccessful in diagnosing the cause of his constant digestive trouble and nagging pains—sometimes sharp, needle-like ones, too. There was only one thing everybody knew for sure: it wasn't a problem with his gallbladder. A surgeon had removed that a month ago but his symptoms had only

1

gotten worse. Most of all, however, Johnny hoped it wasn't what he thought it might be, though he dared not speak its name.

It had been a long day. The couple had been there since early that morning. Emergency patient after emergency patient bumped him back until he was last in line. For hours that felt more like years, he sat on the gurney in a hospital gown, his visor, cargo shorts, golfing shirt, and loafers in a plastic bag on the cold, clean floor next to Patti. He was tired. So very tired. He was unusually quiet, too, having used up all of his sparkle on the pretty nurses who came in throughout the day while Patti sat nearby, trying to ignore their interactions. One sweet, young thing asked him what he did for a living.

"I work up in Lancaster County, mostly with the Amish," Johnny announced proudly in his booming tenor, a voice so resounding he didn't need a microphone when he used to sing solos in church. He crossed his arms over his shrunken belly.

"I'm fascinated with the Amish. What are they like?" she asked, innocent and wide-eyed.

"They're just like you and me!" he said, wanting to dispel all rumors. "Like I tell 'em all the time, 'The only difference between you Amish and us English' —that's what they call anyone who isn't Amish—'is that you guys wear a uniform!' " Johnny laughed at his favorite line. "They just love it." He chuckled and sighed as she bustled around checking on things.

"Yeah, I've got a little bit of a special place up there," he continued mysteriously. Before she could ask what that special place was, he told her: "I'm probably the only English who's been invited to be a guest preacher in the Amish church—twice!" He punctuated the end of his sentence by lifting his bushy old-man eyebrows on his bald, unnaturally tanned head, the result of countless hours upon hours on the golf course, giving him the appearance of being much older than his sixty-three years.

"Wow. So you're a preacher?"

"No, but they call me The Roving Bishop," he joked. "I'm a building inspector."

"Oh," she said, obviously not understanding what he meant but didn't ask what his job entailed.

Johnny was glad. He didn't want to risk losing her attention explaining the dull technicalities, like how all new construction has to follow the state's building code and all new inspectors have to know the code and pass a certification test. He hated explaining how, after becoming certified, inspectors check up on builders in all stages of the process, assuring the state's building code, designed for safety and environmental protection, is being followed; if the builder fails to meet the standards at any stage, the inspector can halt the project until the violation is fixed; once the project passes all phases, the inspector issues a permit for occupancy. He dreaded seeing his audience's eyes glaze over if he talked about how several inspection companies can work in the same area, but each have to be approved by the township where they work. The stories he had about the Amish were much more interesting.

"I used to love that show, *The Amish Mafia*," the pretty blonde nurse said, her blue eyes alive. "Is there really an Amish Mafia?"

He chuckled. While the program that tried to pass itself off as a reality show aired, he got that question quite often and hated how misleading it was. "No!" he said, shaking his head and smiling as if that were an absurd concept. He stopped abruptly, raising his wild, wiry eyebrows again, and answered cryptically, leaning in her direction. "Well, yes, there is an Amish Mafia… but it isn't what you think." He waited for her to take the bait. She bit. Eagerly.

"It's the church. The church is the real Amish Mafia," he announced like it was a big secret that he was finally able to tell, "but that doesn't make for good television." He leaned back again.

Quite curious now, she all but forgot what she came in to do and asked for an explanation.

Johnny, having captured her entire attention, became even more animated and went in for the kill. "You see, the Amish church and the bishops control every aspect of the community life: financial, social, everything. I learned this early on," he started, his bloodshot, blue eyes sparkling, and paused strategically. Then, as if

3

the nurse had asked for the reason, he continued: "This one time I was givin' out a building permit for an addition in an Amish grocery store. The Amishman who owned the grocery store lived right next to it, and he had something like, probably, ten kids, OK?

"Now, normally when they have that many kids, the kids learn to work in the business as soon as they are able to walk and talk, but the wife would not allow the kids to go and work in the grocery store because he hired an eighteen-year-old girl to work in the store. Now, because of what was going on in the grocery store," he said, lowering his head and crinkling his deeply lined forehead, "the eighteen-year-old girl became pregnant. As soon as that happened, the church stepped in and... *took care of it.*"

"What do you mean they took care of it? Like... like the *mafia* mafia?" she asked, her eyes round. Patti looked up from her phone to roll her green ones.

"Well, they sent the man to 'rehab,' " he accented with air quotes, then returned his hands to their original position under his elbows, "and they took all ten kids and the wife and dispersed them all across the United States. And the girl? They sent the girl to *places unknown*," he said, reaching out and wiggling his fingers in illustration, "so that there was no sign that there was ever a problem."

"Oh, wow!" she said, completely engaged. "That's much more interesting than the show. So is it all fake?"

"Well, no, the two kids on the show that make up the 'Mafia'?" he said, again with air quotes. "They grew up in Amish families in Lancaster. My buddy, Antique—he's my head bishop up in Georgetown and a big guy in the Amish church—his son used to run around with them. And the story goes—Antique told me this— the boys were about twelve or thirteen years old on their farm on Bell Road, and their dad got caught in the chopper—which is a piece of farm machinery—and the chopper just chewed him up. And he was layin' there screamin', and they called the rescue people and the rescue people was comin', but the boys stood there as the dad was screamin', 'Please, let me die!' "

4

"Oh my God! How awful!" she said and put a hand over her mouth.

"Yeah, so that was their remembrance of Amish life," Johnny said with a confusing mix of nodding and shaking his head. "Well, they found a way to make big money: they are the 'Amish Mafia,' " he said with air quotes one more time around the name of the TV program, "but there ain't no such thing." He swore this as a fact, scrunching up his deeply wrinkled face. "But boy, oh boy, the television is sellin' it, my goodness! I mean, if you don't act right they're gonna come and they're gonna wreck your buggy?" He rolled his eyes dramatically, mocking the notion. "Let me tell ya— nobody's wreckin' anybody's buggy!"

She looked at him and smiled, then looked over at his wife who was staring at her phone.

"But I get those questions all the time, see, because I'm also the zoning officer in Bart Township up in Lancaster," he said, and again didn't explain the technicalities of that position assuming that it would have gone right over her head anyway.

"Why would they call the zoning officer about it?"

"Because the zoning officer is like… he's like the knower of all things that go on in the township," he explained in the way *he* saw it, at least. Ask anyone else, and they might say this: unlike a building inspector, only one zoning officer is appointed by the supervisors of a township. No knowledge of building code is required, only the specific rules of the township regarding what can be built where. When a builder requests a permit to begin a project that isn't completely clear according to the local law, a public hearing is held in case there are any objections in the community. If there are no issues or objections, a permit for construction is granted. But that's certainly not nearly as glamorous or important sounding.

In Bart, Johnny blurred the lines between his two jobs much of the time. If he issued a zoning permit, he usually offered a package deal with his company, Municipal Solutions, to handle their building inspections also. He shared the company, approved for work in Bart and surrounding townships in Lancaster and Chester counties, with his only son, Young John (with whom he also shared a house).

Johnny, however, wasn't like other building inspectors or zoning officers. Far from it. He was full service. Like a concierge on wheels, he zigzagged through the scenic rolling hills of Lancaster county, rushing around to help his mostly Amish clients gather the pieces of information they needed for their permit puzzles: the applications, the plans, the approval of the plans, even delivering the payments to the correct offices. Sometimes he'd actually draw the plans himself to save his clients money. If their project required zoning, he bundled it. If his company was hired to handle the building inspections on a project that required a zoning permit from another township, he would talk to their zoning officer and handle the paperwork for them. He did this all for not much more than the cost of the inspection services alone.

Before the patient had a chance to tell his nurse about his traumatic first official day as Bart Township's zoning officer that was never far from his mind, another nurse poked her head in the door to see what was taking the young woman so long. She finished up her task in a hurry and rushed out.

Johnny glanced over at his wife sitting beside him, still staring at her phone. For her sake, he hoped that whatever they'd find in the biopsy would be nothing serious. She was really looking forward to her trip the next day. She was going to spend a week with her rich cousins in North Carolina and she'd been saving up for it since Christmas. He was supposed to take her to the airport. He'd hate to be the reason she couldn't go.

Maybe we should've scheduled this test for when she got back, just in case they find something serious, he thought, but what were the chances of that? Anyway, it was too late.

Whatever it is, I'll get through it, he told himself. He had to. That's all there was to it. He wasn't done living. He had people and things to take care of, things he wanted to do still. He'd work really hard on it, and whatever it ended up being would go away. He'd treat it like a job, and he was good at doing jobs.

A different nurse rushed through the doorway. Johnny and

Patti looked up, hope hanging on their faces. "We're finally ready for you, Mr. Coldiron," she said, busily checking his IV.

"Wonderful!" he said with a bright smile, masking his nerves.

As the anesthesia coursed through his 240 lbs., he couldn't hold back the onslaught of negative thoughts from creeping in. *What if I die on the operating table? What if there is a complication that leaves me a vegetable? What if they find something that's incurable and I die a slow, agonizing death?*

With death on his mind, his first day as zoning officer floated to the surface:

It was a beautiful October morning in 2006, full of possibility. The sun shone brightly over the harvested, rolling hills with the promise of peace and rest that fall brings to farming communities, the kind of morning that makes you want to take a deep breath and thank the heavens you're alive.

He had been almost out of Lancaster County on his way to another inspection before he knew anything was wrong. His phone rang, as it always did, atop the permanent stack of code books, forms, and papers next to him that featured his daily list of things to do. It was Grace Hostetter, Bart Township's secretary, the woman who recommended he take over the position she vacated.

"Amazing Grace!" he answered, narrowly missing a buggy. Before he could finish singing the first line to the hymn while winding his way past the razed cornfields, she interrupted.

"Oh, John. Did you hear the news?" Her voice shook.

"No, I don't listen to the news." If it wasn't on a sports station, he didn't know about it. He didn't want to know about the bad stuff he couldn't do anything about.

"Oh, gosh, John, you're not going to believe it," she said, nearly in tears. "We just had a shooting in the Nickel Mines school and girls were killed!"

His heart stopped; he slammed on the brakes. "I'll be right there!" Turning around, he raced back, imagining the bloody scene and wanting to help however he could. How could something like this happen? Why does a loving God allow this? Why? Why? Why? As he got closer to the school, he was so lost in thought he had to slam on his brakes to avoid hitting the blockade.

"I'm sorry, sir, we can't let any non-essential personnel through," the two policemen explained through Johnny's driver side window.

"But I'm the zoning officer!" he said as if somebody's life depended on it.

The two men conferred out of earshot and after noticing his official-looking yellow pickup truck that he got cheap at an auction with the single broken light on top, they decided to let him through. However, in the time it took to give their answer, he had changed his mind, realizing the best way to help would be to get out of the way.

"That's OK, boys," he said. "You have a tough job to do today. There's no need for the zoning officer to be there." He turned around and drove back to where he was going before, his heart five times heavier than when he awoke that morning.

Later, Johnny figured out that he'd been less than a mile away from the scene when the massacre occurred. He was at King's Grocery Store, an Amish market with low ceilings, a musty smell, and dim lighting that featured shelves upon shelves of plastic bags filled with candies and assorted food staples. He had been there doing an inspection on their addition, like any other he'd done in the area over the past couple of years, completely unaware what was happening just down the road.

A deranged milk truck driver had barged into a defenseless one-room Amish schoolhouse at gunpoint, let the adults and boys go, and tied up the remaining female students. When he shot himself it ended the rampage that left five girls dead, five injured, and traumatized the entire nation.

Reporters swarmed the scene like wasps, flying about extending the havoc and chaos in the usually peaceful and insular community. White news vans clogged up one side of the already dangerously narrow, roller coaster-like roads as far as anyone could see; crews with cameras trampled through private yards like they had a right.

Being his very first day as Bart Township's zoning officer

when the shooting took place, Johnny had few answers for the endless questions from the press, but instinctively did his best to help and protect the unique community he knew little about.

"I'm sorry, I don't know where the girls are being schooled," he told reporters after one of the fathers, Amos King, had called to let him know they were holding classes temporarily in his three car garage.

"Yes, the schoolhouse will be torn down on Friday at noon," he told another after learning it would be demolished late Thursday night.

Just as the swarm was dying down, the press caught wind that the Amish were actually forgiving the shooter—something Johnny couldn't understand. It caused a sensation and captured the imagination of the whole world who sent donation after donation.

Ever since that horrific day that still burned inside his soul, Grace would say to him, "You were put here for a reason, you know that?" He always brushed it off with a chuckle but secretly suspected the same thing and assumed the Amish believed it, too. What else would explain why they took to him like they did? They usually weren't so open with the English (or at least that's what he'd always heard). They would tell him everything—even things he didn't want to know. But why him? Why was he put there that day? What was he supposed to be doing? For nearly nine years he wondered this, all the while collecting stories along the way and helping out however he could.

Johnny's eyelids grew heavier and heavier as the nurses wheeled him out of the room and down the long hallway. When he couldn't keep his baby blues open any longer, he hoped against hope he hadn't just closed them for the last time.

Johnny and Patti, 2015

Johnny and Patti, cir. 1985

CHAPTER 2

October 1996 – December 2014

There had been clues that all was not well. Seven months earlier as the Amish sold apple cider and winter squash at their farmer's markets, Johnny traipsed across his field in Oxford, Pennsylvania to the old horse barn to change a lightbulb for his wife late one October afternoon. There, as he stretched to the ceiling, standing up on top of the ten-foot ladder to screw in the bulb, he experienced a pain so intense and foreign he couldn't tell if he were being electrocuted or stabbed. Somehow, by the grace of God, he managed not to fall and dragged himself back to his basement apartment to lie down.

The next day he was shocked when he couldn't walk. So was everyone else. He had enjoyed nearly perfect health and boundless energy his whole life, only ever missing a handful of work days due to illness. That alone should have been enough of a clue, but it wasn't. The day after that he managed, through pure force of will, to stumble around and get some work done on the playset he was building for the grandkids, firmly believing that when old people stop working, that's when they die. He didn't want to stop working. He didn't want to die.

When, in the months that followed, he began turning down invitations for free golf because he "wasn't feeling good," it should have been an even bigger clue that something was wrong. Unfortunately, it wasn't either. He was going to live forever. Eventually his body would heal itself, and as long as he ignored whatever it was, sooner or later it would go away. He pretended he was fine and struggled to continue on as always.

Before that October afternoon in the barn, he had zoomed through the routine of his life. Every morning he would wake up before dawn with his wife still in bed, drink a pot of coffee, black, make a list of things to do for the day, and visit his mother twenty minutes away to say hello. She'd feed him biscuits and gravy (whether he wanted it or not) and he'd drink a couple more cups of coffee with her. Back into his little yellow pickup truck with the light on top he'd go and speed toward Amishland.

Amishland: where horse-drawn plows, wagons, and carriages (or "buggies") are still more common than cars. The appearance of these particular Pennsylvanians working in their stores, fields, and gardens look like paintings of people from a time before photography. Picturesque farms, each with a house and at least one red barn with a silo, dot the graceful, rolling hillsides. Almost any day of the year when the sun is out, black and plain-colored clothes can be seen in all sizes, hanging on lines that stretch from every house to the top of their nearest barn or garage. If not for the occasional car or delivery truck, one could be convinced that time travel is possible in Lancaster.

Amish clothesline (photo by Terry Tabb)

Most days Johnny would roll in and around the tiny village

of Georgetown in Bart Township of Lancaster County, where he served the 80 percent Old Order Amish population as their zoning officer. Between rounds he would sometimes stop by the Antique store to visit "Antique," the bishop who owned and operated it (hence his nickname), then ride a fraction of a mile up the road to see his buddy, Dan Stoltzfus of Hometown Builders, though rarely with a reason other than to say hello and get the latest town gossip.

Occasionally, he'd walk through to the other side of the building that Dan owned with his Mennonite cousin, and into The Hometown Kitchen where everyone in the community—Amish and English alike—came to eat and commune. Sometimes he'd grab a bite to eat, but almost always he would see someone he knew and have to tell his latest, greatest story like a popular song on heavy rotation that gets played over and over on the radio.

Every now and then there would be a fire. From The Hometown Kitchen's large front windows, the inspector and other customers could watch the fire trucks load up and speed away with Amishmen hanging off the back. But unlike in other parts of the country, no one ever looked up from their sandwiches to watch the horses that constantly trotted by pulling gray and black buggies with large orange caution triangles on the back and at least one child staring out the rear window.

From inspection to inspection Johnny would dart, checking up on builders and buildings in all stages of construction—footers, framing, roofing—all the while his phone ringing nonstop with calls for new business. "Where are ya?" he'd ask. If the caller was nearby, he'd stop over right away, impressing the customer with his quick service. If the caller was too far away, he'd pass the phone to his shoulder, and with one hand scribble down the new name on his list perched atop the permanent stack of books beside him, dodging horse and buggies with the other.

If ever there was a new name on his list that he didn't know (which happened infrequently after so much time), the inspector got a chance to tell him or her about his first day as zoning officer. "My very first day working here in Bart was the exact same day the girls were shot in the school," he would say in a near whisper to convey

13

the solemnity and significance of what he was sure was not simply a coincidence.

After work—and depending on the season—he'd golf with his buddies, or mend fences at the old farm, or mow the lawn. More often than not, he'd take his wife out to dinner with friends and tell story after story usually involving an Amishman, or a golf club, and sometimes both. Once back at home, he'd sit down in his brown cloth recliner and doze off in front of the sports network. The next day he'd do it all over again.

When he first took the zoning officer position in Bart, his home was in the 250-year-old, three-story brick colonial farmhouse across the field where he had lived with his wife since their early 20's and raised four children. A few years after working in Bart, he sold their house and barns to their middle daughter, Brooke, for a song—much to his wife's dismay; selling the property had been their retirement plan. With nothing left, he moved across the field to the basement apartment of his son's McMansion, part of the new development on ground that had once been part of the farm's original 174 acres. "I tell the Amish all the time that I live in a Granny Flat. They know what that is!" Johnny would say.

He finished out his new home himself, laying the faux hardwood floors, hanging the drywall, installing the kitchen and bathroom, and wiring everything. In the living room he arranged his leather couch and tables around his most important piece of furniture —his recliner—making sure to point it toward his second most important possession—his new flat-screen TV. In the crowded space, large bay windows faced the west, overlooking the grassy backyard that he loved to mow. The view rivaled the sports network when his grandkids played on the swings attached to the balcony right outside the window or rode the white mini-pony back and forth over makeshift jumps.

Outside he landscaped around the entire place with various bushes and trees and fenced in the backyard for his dogs, Happy and Duke, to run around in. He laid a brick pathway that started at the garage at the end of the driveway and wrapped around the left side of the house toward the back with a 90 degree turn in the middle.

There, a sign hung on the fence that said "Grandmother and Granddad Coldiron" pointing to the right and down the steps to the back door. Along the pathway he planted all sorts of perennials such as irises, lilies, liriope, black-eyed susans, and never die; decorative grasses surrounded a waterfall that trickled into a microscopic fish pond. Each spring he sowed a small vegetable garden on the other side of the house with cucumbers and squash; tomatoes were planted at the top of the walkway next to the ever-bearing strawberries that he intended for the grandkids to enjoy.

He decorated the inside, too. On the maroon and cream-colored walls he hung sports memorabilia, ceramics his grandchildren made in art class, portraits of his wife's family, and a framed poster of Will Rogers who proclaimed "I've never met a man I didn't like." On another wall hung his favorite quote by Hunter S. Thompson: "Life should not be a journey to the grave with the intention of arriving safely in a pretty and well preserved body, but rather to skid in broadside in a cloud of smoke, thoroughly used up, totally worn out, and loudly proclaiming 'Wow! What a Ride!' "

Johnny called it home; Patti only did so reluctantly.

The sign at the bend in the walkway to the apartment

CHAPTER 3

January 2015

It wasn't until well after the new year that Johnny suspected he might not actually live forever. Sure, no one ever had, but if there ever was a first, he'd be it. He was special, different—at least that's what the Amish always told him.

One icy-cold day in January just as the sun peeked over the trees in the east, he finished his pot of black coffee and left for work. With his list of things to do for the day in hand, he struggled, brick by brick, up the frost-covered pathway. With his breath short and visible in the chilly air, he wound around his son's two-story brick house to the two-car garage at the top of the steep slope in the yard. Slowly, he continued across the blacktop to where his pickup truck sat in the grass beside the short driveway, and wished summer would hurry up and get there. He was sick and tired of the cold.

After a quick visit to his mother, he sped away to Lancaster County where icicles hung from the bare trees and snow blanketed the farmland. Everything sparkled. At the crest of a hill he swerved to miss a buggy and nearly hit a patch of ice. His adrenaline surged and his side ached like no other pain he'd ever experienced. His hand touched his collarbone to examine the lump growing there. In the past few months it had appeared and grown to half the size of a mini-marshmallow. He couldn't explain it.

However, he could explain his weight loss and dwindling energy: he couldn't eat; most everything made him gassy and uncomfortable. The list of foods that were giving him trouble was now longer than the ones that weren't. He didn't think it was odd, but those who knew him did. After one of his annual golfing trips years ago, he told the story of eating a $16 "Gorilla" sundae that consisted of two bananas, eight scoops of ice cream, and a whole can of whipped cream just to get his name on the wall of the parlor, *after* consuming a full rack of ribs for dinner. The other golfer who attempted this feat threw up in the bushes halfway through his sundae while Johnny sucked down a vanilla shake just to show off.

Most recently he had developed a nasty cough.

With his mortality on his mind, he called his oldest daughter, Audra, who lately had taken to giving books she created as presents, and ran his latest idea by her. "You know, people are always tellin' me I should write a book with all my stories, and I'm like, 'I can't write a book!' but then I started thinkin'… I started thinkin' maybe *you* can help me." If he wasn't going to live forever, perhaps his stories could, then in a way he would live on, too.

"We could have the one about the fire trucks that had to go the long way around to the fire because they couldn't pass by the bishop." The fire truck driver had quit being Amish (hence he was able to drive the truck) but stayed a fireman. If their bishop, who stood at the nearby corner to direct traffic when the siren went off, saw the other Amish firemen on the truck not shunning the driver, they'd get in trouble. Big trouble.

"And we could have the one about Mose. I told you that one, right? Mick Jagger?" It was his latest, greatest story about an Amishman who, during his Rumspringa, the period of freedom during adolescence, toured Texas playing in a rock band.

"Yeah, you did. But I don't understand," Audra said, confused. "How did he have band practice without electricity?"

"Oh! They've all got propane generators in the barns. Every one of 'em. Some of 'em even keep computers in there," he explained.

"Wait. But I thought they weren't allowed to have electricity and modern technology. How do they have computers?" Audra asked like her whole world suddenly turned upside down.

17

"Well, they aren't *supposed* to have computers in their homes, but some do and they just hide them from the bishops. But a lot of the Amish have found a loop-hole and partner with Mennonites, so they can have all that stuff in their businesses," he said about the denomination of Christianity that shares historical roots with the Amish but differs in their attitude toward modern technology. "One of my hard-line bishops was complainin' to me just the other day, he said, 'John, they're all goin' into business with their Mennonite relatives so they can use electricity, and I don't like it!'" Johnny chuckled. "And I told my buddy, Dan, about that and he goes, 'Hey! That's me and Abe!'

"But most of 'em, even if they aren't partnered with an English, can have telephones in their businesses now and even their homes. They just don't answer the phone, and you have to leave a message and they'll call you back. It used to be that none of 'em had phones in their homes, and the ones that still don't, they have a little phone booth at the end of their driveway or in the barn—somewhere they can't hear it ring so it doesn't interfere with family time. And it's funny, because those guys will give you business cards with the times of the day you can reach them on the phone and that's when they'll stand out in their phone shanties and wait for calls," he laughed and continued. "But more and more of 'em have phones in the house now and it's OK as long as they can't hear it ring. Even the bishops have 'em!"

"Really?"

"Oh, yeah. There was this one time when I first started here in Bart and I was talkin' to Antique—he's my other hard-line bishop, and a big guy in the bishop's council—and I needed some more information about this guy in his church he wanted me to help, and he goes, 'Hold on. I'll call him right now,' and he went into his house! I couldn't believe it!" Johnny laughed and chuckled.

"Yeah, so that's been my favorite part of the job—seein' the cultural change. They want to pretend it's not happening, but it is. I see things—and I tell my bishop in Georgetown all the time, I tell him, 'You don't even want to know all the things I know!' And he goes, 'Oh, don't tell me, John. Please don't tell me!' I see kids on scooters who have smart phones, and they tell me they'd give up the church before they'd give up MLB."

"What's the MLB?"

"C'mon, Audra! You don't know what the MLB is?" he said, pretending to be disappointed in her. "It's Major League Baseball, geez!" She should have known since his whole life had involved baseball in some way or another, having once aspired to be a major league pitcher. After he tore a tendon in his right elbow effectively ending any prospects he might have had, he coached every type of ball team around, including little league. He enrolled Audra in it for two years and watched her do cartwheels in the outfield.

He paused and sighed with one hand on the wheel, his eyes on the countryside. "Upp! There's another Amish farm with solar panels," he said like it was no big deal, knowing his daughter would think otherwise.

"What? The Amish have solar panels?"

"Oh, yeah. A lot of 'em do."

"How is *that* allowed?"

"Well, see, they're not actually as cut-and-dried as you might think. A big reason they don't use electricity is they would have to hook up to the electric grid and be dependent on the English, and they don't want that. But if they can generate their own electric by windmills or solar panels, that's OK. But, of course, not all the bishops agree on that because they know as soon as things like TVs and computers become commonplace, it'll drastically change the home life from what they have now and that's what they fight against. And that's a big reason, too, why they don't drive cars or ride bikes: the family could get too far apart."

"Oh, that's interesting. I always thought it had something to do with religion, like they thought God hated technology or something," Audra said, surprise in her voice.

"No, no. Not really. So anyway, Mose's band used to practice in the barn, and I asked him because I know his dad. I said, 'How did your dad like that?' He shook his head and he goes, 'Oh, he didn't like it one bit!' Now, of course, all this was *before* Mose became Amish."

19

"*Became* Amish?" Audra asked, surprised again. "You mean you're not just born Amish? I had always thought you were born into it, like being Jewish."

"No, you have to choose to be. You have to accept the church and its ways and then you're Amish. Before that you can do anything anyone else can," he explained.

"Oh, really? So could anyone just choose to be Amish? Like, could I be Amish if I wanted to be?" Audra's siblings had long teased her that she and her husband might as well be Amish with their homesteading lifestyle.

Johnny chuckled. "No, I don't think so, but I did hear about this one guy who turned Amish to marry his wife. I'm like, 'Oh my God, I've *got* to meet her! She must be one good lookin' lady to turn Amish for!' " he cackled.

"Dad! Don't be the dirty old man!"

"Oh, I'm just havin' fun!" he swore with a chuckle. "And, of course, if you change your mind *after* you become Amish, that's when you get into trouble and the shunning starts. If you leave the Amish church, your family and Amish friends aren't supposed to talk to you or have anything to do with you. Anyway, Mose said when he came home from playin' in Texas, he just decided to be Amish. So I said to him, I says, 'Mose, don't you have a guitar that you just pick on every now and then?' He goes, 'Oh no, John, that's not allowed.' " He swerved again to miss a buggy, speeding along with one hand on the wheel and the other holding his phone to his ear.

"Why is that?"

"Because they are the Old Order Amish and don't have any sort of instruments in church, kinda like the way your Mamaw was raised in the mountains. Oh, Mamaw could have easily been Amish and been very happy," he said about his mother. "Now, Mose—he never married—and he was the one who handled the money when the girls were shot in the school and the English world started sendin' donations. He's *very* good with money. He offered me a big sum of money if I could get a Wawa on a piece of ground he owns," he said, referencing the popular convenience store chain and paused to dodge another buggy.

"We can also have the time I was interviewed by CNN in there."

Six months after "The Happening" as the affected community calls it, when the school house was rebuilt in a new, nearby location, the media swarm revisited for opening day ceremonies, pestering Johnny again with question after question, even bugging him at home.

"This is the eighth time you've called," Patti told the reporter, annoyed that they kept interrupting her favorite reality shows. "My husband is asleep and he doesn't wake up for anybody!"

This time around Bart's zoning officer knew more about the people he served, having ingratiated himself. Suspecting that he might be filmed, Johnny dressed up wearing a top with a pocket instead of his usual golfing shirt, and even removed his visor from his sun-damaged, bald head.

"The Amish people are so pitiful," he remembered the young female reporter saying who sat across from him in the tiny township office, pointing a giant microphone toward his face.

He started laughing his big laugh that easily filled the narrow room. "What in the world are you talkin' about?" he asked as if that was the craziest thing he'd ever heard.

"Well, they don't have cars," she clarified. "They drive horse drawn carriages."

"Are you kiddin' me? Let me ask you this," he said. Then, in an effort to shock and surprise her, he turned his head sideways and peered at her through one eye like his childhood hero, Popeye, scrunching up his face: "how did you get down here from New York?"

She told him they drove.

"Yeah, well, the Amish do have cars," he said, "and when they go somewhere they have what they call a 'driver.' In your world, that would be called a chauffeur." He checked to see if she was sufficiently impressed then continued with a sly grin, "You didn't have that, did ya?"

"Excuse me, Mr. Coldiron," she said politely, uncomfortably adjusting herself in the fold up chair, "but they don't have electricity."

"Well, how much time do ya have? I can take you around to any number of farms around here that run on solar electric," he said, trying to really blow her mind. Again with the one-eyed squint he leaned forward and added, "How advanced are you?"

He was proud of the comebacks he had for all of her questions. She clearly thought the Amish people were poor, and he knew they were not; they spent their money on what they wanted to have, not what the rest of the world thought they should have.

Finally she asked him, mostly out of frustration, if there was anything—*anything* at all unusual about the new school.

"Yes," he broke down and admitted. "They bricked the school instead of the usual plain construction of vinyl siding over wood."

When she asked why he thought they did that, in an effort to not mention that it was probably because of all the money the English world had sent, he uttered the words that rang in his ears for years afterward: "Well, I don't know... Maybe it's so the Big Bad Wolf won't blow it down!"

That was the only bit CNN aired of the entire interview, and even now, he cringed in embarrassment over the comment. His only consolation was that his adopted community—the Amish—didn't see it.

Audra agreed to help with the book and instructed him to start writing down his stories. "Write them down?" he asked, not having expected to have to actually do anything other than talk. A sharp pain stabbed him in the side as he hung up and dodged another buggy. He had little idea that soon he would have the fight of his life.

Old Order Amish buggy (photo by Terry Tabb)

Amishman plowing his field with mules (photo by Terry Tabb)

CHAPTER 4

Early February

Ignoring the pain, Johnny turned right at the corner before Antique's store where the bishop would stand to direct traffic when the siren went off. He drove a short distance to the Hometown Kitchen's lot across from the fire hall, and pulled around back to Hometown Builders' snow-lined parking lot for a quick visit to Dan Stoltzfus as horses pulling buggies trotted by.

Johnny couldn't remember exactly when he met the Stoltzfuses, but since Dan's company had been in charge of rebuilding the infamous schoolhouse and Johnny had handled the township's zoning and the building inspections, he figured it was probably then. In that time Johnny had come to regard Dan and his wife, Liz, as his best friends in the area. Once he even gave them a ride to their mountain vacation home, then drove one of their daughters back so she could go to the beach the next day with some of her teen-aged friends.

"Hey, Danny boy!" the inspector said in his big voice as he entered the brightly lit and whirring office that looked like any other construction office: a drop ceiling, white walls with corkboards, papers hanging from them haphazardly, flimsy-looking tables with blueprints draped across them like tablecloths.

The tall, thin man with a long, graying beard and suspenders buttoned to his black stovepipe pants, got up from his computer and hobbled over to shake his friend's hand. "Hallo John," he said in his

Pennsylvania Dutch accent, "How are you?"

"What's with the limp, man?"

Before Dan could answer, his wife, Liz, having heard the question on her way in from the back, answered for him: "He was playin' ice hockey with the boys last night and fell!"

"I was just about to score!"

"John, tell him he's too old for that kinda stuff. Maybe he'll listen to you." The petite woman in the simple blue dress and bonnet went about her business rinsing out a coffee cup on the other side of the partition. Dan managed to sit back down and swiveled his chair around to face the table in the middle of the space, where he tried, out of habit, to lift his feet up on, but stopped and winced.

"Well, I'm next!" Johnny said loudly in Liz's direction so she could hear.

"Next for what?" Dan asked, ready to laugh.

"I'm next in line for Liz when you kill yourself doin' somethin' stupid!" He laughed big at his own joke. Liz shook her head and suppressed a grin.

"Dan, seriously, there comes a time when you have to give up on doin' young buck stuff!"

"Oh, is that so?" Dan smirked. "How old were you?"

"I was forty-seven. I tore my Achilles tendon playin' basketball. The only reason I got it fixed was because it was messin' up my golf swing!"

"Well, I'm not quite there yet." Dan chuckled, clasped his hands behind his head, and leaned back in his chair. Liz set a cup of coffee on the desk beside him and offered one to Johnny, who declined since he'd already had the equivalent of a pot so far.

"It looks like the Beiler house is about done," Dan said after taking a sip.

"Yep, that's on my list. I'm actually headed up there after I leave here for their final inspection," Johnny said and started to laugh. "Hey, did I ever tell you about Mrs. Beiler callin' me when they were tearin' down the old house? She goes, 'John. How much do you think I can get on eBay for the doorknob to the room where Harrison Ford slept?' I was like, 'Wait a second! How in the world does an Amish lady know about Harrison Ford and eBay?' " The Beilers had bought the farm that had served as a set for the 80's movie, *Witness*.

Johnny laughed an enormous belly laugh, throwing his head back, initiating a huge coughing fit from deep within his burning lungs. Dan and Liz looked at each other with worried glances. Liz offered him a glass of water but he refused that, too, insisting he was fine. She asked him if he'd seen a doctor about his persistent cough. When he said he hadn't, she suggested he visit the community's new medical center that he had a hand in bringing to the area.

"No, I don't need a doctor—I'm fine," he insisted again. "Remind me to tell you the one about my engineer and the medical center later." Johnny sat down in the chair across the table from Dan. "Honest to God, you just can't make this stuff up," he sighed with a smile and leaned back chuckling to himself.

"Hey," Johnny said, sitting up suddenly, remembering they hadn't yet heard his latest story, "how come you guys never told me Mose was Mick Jagger?"

"Huh?" Dan asked, confused.

"So the other day I'm over at Mose's office," Johnny started eagerly, "and we're talkin' about the Nickel Mines project. And I'm tellin' him about how one of my supervisors who lives across the street is tryin' to get a four-way stop put there even after my engineer already said there wasn't enough traffic to warrant one. And Mose goes, he says, 'You know where there are a lot of four-way stops, John? Texas.' I'm thinkin', 'What does an Amishman in a wheelchair know about Texas?'

"So I go over to the next stop on my list, an English builder, and I tell him what Mose said because, you know, I kep' thinkin' how weird it was that he would know anything about four-way stops in Texas, and he goes, 'Yeah, but do you know what he was *doin'* in Texas?' I said, 'No.' He goes, 'He was playin' rock-n-roll!' " Johnny screamed the punchline then doubled over in his chair, laughing and cackling and slapping his knee.

"You didn't know that?" Dan grinned.

"Noooo!" Johnny cried as if a big secret had been withheld

from him for years.

"Yah, I heard he did Tom Petty better than Tom Petty," he said and took another sip of his coffee. "How is that Nickel Mines project going, anyway? Has your supervisor who lives across from it been givin' ya any trouble?"

"Bill? No, Bill's fine. I'm not worried about him," he said, wanting to believe it. "He told me if I could get that old building torn down, he didn't care what I did, and I got it torn down. Case closed. I just wished I'd taken a picture of that place. It was just awful."

Johnny remembered the property in question well. It had been the community's biggest eyesore, a hundred-year-old, dilapidated building at the edge of a well-traveled crossroads. A century ago, the building stood strong as a shining example of progress, the county's first self-serve grocery store that supplied the once bustling mining town. With the mine long since abandoned, the building eventually had been, too.

"Well, how about Gabriel? Has he been behavin' himself?"

Just hearing the name, Gabriel Glick, was enough to elicit a sigh and an eye roll from the inspector. Mr. Glick, the largest and most unpopular Amish landowner in the area, had purchased the property and tore down the old building. That, at least, pleased everyone.

"No, no," Johnny insisted, "Gabe listens to me now ever since that time I caught him tryin' to cheat and made him rip out all the plumbing. I told you about that one, didn't I?"

"What's this story?" Liz asked from the kitchen. "I don't think I've heard this one."

"Oh, this is a good one," he said, ready to launch into it when his phone rang. He saw the name and immediately answered.

"Antiiiiique! What's up, man? Hey—do you need advice about the church again, because you know I'm not Amish, right?" Dan and Liz snickered at the ridiculous question while Johnny laughed big over something his friend said on the other end of the line.

The inspector felt honored to be needed by such an important man in the community whose opinions mattered. Not only was he a

27

bishop in the Amish church, but a high-ranking bishop in the bishop's council that governed Amish communities far and wide, deciding on policies such as whether to allow telephones or bicycles.

"Are ya sure you don't need me to be a guest preacher?" Johnny teased again then began another round of coughing. "Yeah, yeah, I'm fine. Listen, I'll be right over. Is that cool? ... OK... See ya then, buddy. Talk to ya," He hung up and put his phone back in his pocket.

"Hey!" Johnny shouted to his favorite Amish couple as he stood up with great effort thanks to his arthritic knee. "Antique says you guys all think I'm Amish! You know what I always say, right?"

"I don't know, John. You say a lot of things," Liz quipped.

He limped through the kitchen on his way to the restaurant side for their bathrooms and nearly screamed the punchline: "I always say the only difference between you Amish and us English is that you guys all wear a uniform!"

The uniform, black pants, suspenders, and plain, woven shirts with no pockets for men and boys, and long, plain cotton woven dresses for women and girls, was clearly visible on every Amish family's clothesline. Men and boys sport straw hats atop bowl haircuts, while women and girls grow their hair long and tie it in the back into a bun with the part down the middle. Teen girls and women cover their buns with see-through bonnets with white straps that hang down past the shoulders; married men grow beards, but never mustaches. Shoes and boots are always black, and dresses and shirts are always a plain, solid color. White shirts are only for church, weddings, and funerals, and straw hats are only for outdoors. Suspenders, dresses, aprons, shirts, and pants are fastened with buttons or straight pins but never hooks, clamps, or zippers. All coats are plain, long, and black.

Johnny laughed at his own wit while the Stoltzfuses chuckled at his amusement over it. "When's your birthday?" he heard Dan shout as he disappeared into the other side. "I'll get you the hat!"

Though he and Dan had the running joke that all the inspector needed to be Amish was the hat, Johnny would never actually wear one because "it would be disrespectful," and that was not how he was raised. He was raised to be honest, helpful, hard working, and church-going—and he was all those things... except now for church-going. He still believed in what his conservative Southern Baptist upbringing had taught him, but after his dad died right before the turn of the century, he had become more and more disillusioned with organized religion and hadn't been back since. This was a sharp reversal from the days when he insisted his family go Sunday mornings, Sunday nights, and Wednesday evenings.

Every once in awhile when he'd make his nearly daily morning visit to his mother's house for coffee and biscuits and gravy, she would say in her squeaky hillbilly voice, "Now, Johnny, I'm tellin' ya, ya need to get back in church!" "I know, Mom," was all he'd say, though he didn't agree and had no intentions of returning. The truth was, he felt closer to God on the golf course than in a church any Sunday.

On his way out of the bathroom, Abe Stoltzfus, Dan's slight, dark haired, clean shaven Mennonite cousin and business partner, spotted the zoning officer. Abe ran the restaurant and stopped Johnny to tell him about their tentative plans for expansion, and to ask what permits they'd need. He then showed the zoning officer around outside to point out and explain what they were thinking about doing. Before next winter they wanted to move the chiropractor's office, currently practicing in the same building as the restaurant and construction business, to their rental house next door. They also wanted to pave its front yard for parking, and, at the same time, install dry wells in their own parking to improve the stormwater runoff. Johnny loved the idea of the dry wells since he figured it would likely solve many drainage issues in the area and assured Abe that when the time came he'd "take care of yas."

As the inspector climbed slowly and stiffly back into his truck, his lungs tickled and he couldn't hold back another round of burning coughs. Once the fit ended, he drove a few miles down the twisty road past the garden radish patches that almost every Amish residence featured in the winter to aerate the soil, and stopped by the Beilers' farm to perform their final inspection. While doing so he asked about the new house, the kids, and the new baby; they thanked him again for his help in making their living situation possible.

Johnny had long since assumed that one of the reasons he had been put there in Bart on that infamous day was to help; one of the ways he helped was to solve problems for the people of the community whether he benefited or not (and he usually didn't).

He had solved a problem for the Beilers. Dan had told him about their situation. They had wanted to tear down their horribly drafty old farmhouse and live in their carriage house above the barn while they rebuilt. Trouble was, installing a bathroom in the carriage house would technically make it a second dwelling on the property which was not allowed, and no one nearby could house a family of twelve—soon to be thirteen—for that long.

Johnny went to the hearing in the neighboring township with the very pregnant Mrs. Beiler, and gave the officials his word that he would keep an eye on the project, promising it would not become a permanent dwelling on his watch. His heart swelled with pride remembering the hearing board ruling that "if John Coldiron gives us his word, that's good enough for us."

He used to do more of that kind of thing until some officials in other townships became suspicious and accused Johnny of "helping too much." The English didn't want to admit it, but they were jealous of the prosperity the Amish enjoyed while they were mired deep in a recession.

Johnny shifted gears and sped toward Antique's place, eager to see what the bishop wanted. Dodging buggies on the way, he drove by the Nickel Mines project, surprised it hadn't turned into a bigger problem already. Mr. Glick had torn down the old building like he'd been asked, and its replacement had been completed for months without so much as a peep from Bill. However, the second building—the one Bill knew nothing about—was scheduled to break ground in a couple weeks when Johnny would be in Florida on his annual golfing trip. That was one of the reasons he was going despite his health; he didn't want to be around when the horse manure hit the fan.

The inspector pulled into the small paved space beside the Antique furniture store, a converted two-story house built early in the last century, and idled there like always. In a few minutes, a short man around his age, dressed in black, emerged. Sporting a straw hat and a long, gray, untrimmed beard that framed happy eyes, he bounced down the porch steps and landed beside Johnny's driver side window.

"Hey man! You sellin' any antiques?" the inspector shouted in his big, joking voice.

"No, no one wants to come out in this cold!" answered the bishop with a smile. He asked the inspector if he could help with a problem a member of his church was having: he wanted to build a barn for his daughter's wedding (she being one of the survivors of the school shooting), and the board had flat out told him "no."

"Are you kiddin' me? Do you mean to tell me there are so many Amish now you have to have weddings all year round?" he said, trying to get a rise. "It's bad enough that this whole township shuts down from November to February!' " Johnny laughed at his own joke.

Antique giggled in his odd, high-pitched way and assured his friend that the man was just getting ready for next November when wedding season started.

"You know, Antique, if you Amish would just vote, you could run your townships and you wouldn't have these problems." With the majority of the population Amish, it was absolutely true.

"It's just not our way," Antique reminded him, but Johnny couldn't understand it. He collected the necessary information, said goodbye, and darted in front of a buggy as it clip-clopped its way down the road with a long line of cars trailing it, the horse's breath visible in the cold air. He was off to solve another problem but began to get the feeling that all wasn't well.

CHAPTER 5

Mid February – March

In the weeks leading up to his golfing trip, Johnny's health worsened. Not only could he barely eat or sleep, now he struggled to walk and even breath. However, there was no way in the world he would ever consider canceling on his friends and letting them down. He figured the only excuse they'd accept was death, anyway. Years ago when he had torn his Achilles tendon, his long-time pal, Dave Huston, a tall, slender man, five years Johnny's senior whom he met at softball tryouts in the late 70's, still talked him into playing a round the next day. Same thing happened when he stepped on a nail while helping his church with a renovation project and his foot swelled up so big he couldn't even wear a shoe. Now they joked that if a golfer died on the course, they'd play through.

Before heading home from Lancaster Thursday afternoon for his early departure the next morning, he went by the Nickel Mines project one last time with a bad feeling about it, and coughed the whole way back. Patti pleaded with him again to consider not going, aware of the futility.

When Johnny stumbled through the door of his basement apartment after his long weekend in Florida, his wife was shocked at how pale and weak he looked. Never in their long marriage had she seen him appear so fragile. He coughed so much, she briefly considered knocking him over the head with her giant horse-print purse and dragging him to the emergency room. She begged him to let her make a doctor's appointment in the morning. But even with the promise he made to his other long-time buddy, Frank Parrish, only a couple hours old, and even having signed up for health insurance before he left, he still couldn't bring himself to go through with it.

Finally, after struggling for breath on a morning inspection. he got scared. Begrudgingly, he went to the doctor, got the medicine, and for days stayed in his recliner in front of the sports network. As he passed in and out of consciousness, only struggling to get up to go to the bathroom, his phone rang non-stop with most of the calls going straight to voicemail.

Huston and Frank called a couple times each to make sure he had gone to the doctor and to see how he was feeling. Patti made sure he took his medicine like she did for her clients in her elder care job, and went about her usual routine of elder sitting, cleaning out horse stalls, and watching TV.

Near the end of the week his cough was getting better. Though he hadn't eaten much in days, Friday morning, well or not, he dragged himself out of the recliner, determined to get something done. He moved to the round table behind him, much too big for the space, wedged between the recliner and the bookshelf, and sat down heavily in the only chair there was room for. There, beside the stacks of papers so high they threatened to, at any moment, bury him in an avalanche of old lists, bills, and permit applications, he composed his list of things to do for the day. Then, with much more effort than he was used to, he trudged up the barren brick pathway to the truck and in a half an hour he was in Georgetown.

***

Less than a mile from the center of the tiny, old town, the modest Bart Township building stood, nestled among bare oaks and elms, appearing more like an auto repair shop or a service station without the gas pumps than a government building. A garage that housed the township's two road crew vehicles consumed most of the white cinder-block structure's square footage, with the long narrow office that hosted the CNN interview nearly a decade earlier squeezed into the left like an afterthought of the architect.

Johnny parked in front of the office and got out slowly, one leg at a time, managing the few punishing steps across the gravel lot toward the entrance. He twisted the knob and pushed the door open, letting the brisk air blow in. Grace looked over from her desk at the far end of the gray, faux-wood paneled room where she had been busily clicking away on the computer, and squinted.

"John?" she asked as if her eyes might be deceiving her. An enormously relieved smile covered her face, temporarily disguising her worry lines, as she turned her chair toward the man she loved almost as much as her husband.

"Hey Grace!" he said to his plump, silver-haired coworker in the sweet voice that he reserved for women and children.

"Oh John, you don't know how glad I am to see you! When you didn't come in for a few days I was real worried about you," she said, nearly tearing up, "You'd been coughin' so much, I was sure somethin' horrible happened to you."

"Somethin' horrible *did* happen to me!" Johnny said, trying his best to put on a happy face to mask his pain. "I finished dead last!"

"What? You mean on your golfing trip?"

"Oh, geez, Grace, it was awful. *I* was awful." He limped closer, shaking his head; he couldn't believe it himself.

When Grace asked him what he meant, he explained: "I really don't remember much at all, but what I remember most is there was this new guy with us on the trip. He came with me and Frank back to Philadelphia on the plane, and Frank—he's real talkative," Johnny described his tall, long-time friend with an easy smile and a full head of hair that was only now going gray. "He kept tellin' the new guy, he goes, 'You don't understand, you didn't see the real J.D.'," he said, referring to himself the way his golfing buddies did. " 'What you saw is nothin' like J.D. J.D. normally shoots the best!' And I'm like, 'Man, Frank's making excuses for me? I must have been just awful!' "

34

"Oh, John, you couldn't have been that bad," Grace insisted.

"Well, I only played once in the past few months because I've been feelin' so bad. Now, of course, not bein' able to walk coulda had su'um to do with comin' in last, too!"

"You couldn't walk?" she asked, her brows nearly touching.

"No, I mean, it was a struggle just to put one foot in front of the other. This one night we went to a fancy restaurant and, of course, they're all just hoppin' in the elevator and goin' up to the top floor and they're all there waitin' for me, and my one golfin' buddy, Ronnie, he looks at me and says, 'J.D., you can't walk!' I said, 'Hey man, just give me time. I can make it. Just give me time!'

"And when we got back to Philly, Frank said—and he was tryin' to be apologetic because he knows I'm just a hard-headed hillbilly," Johnny said, describing himself in the way that whenever his wife heard it, she would remind him that he grew up in Landenberg, Pennsylvania. "He says, 'I hate to tell you this, but the boys said I'm responsible for makin' sure you get to the doctor.' I said, 'Frank, I promise you, if I can just get home—please, Lord, let me get home—I'll go to the doctor.' "

"Goodness, John. Tell me you went to the doctor," said Grace, hanging on his every word.

"Yeah, I did, but not right away. I went up to do an inspection in Peach Bottom the next morning when I got back—it was on the second floor of this old Amish farmhouse—and when I got up there I felt like all the air had been sucked out of the room. I couldn't breathe. It really scared me. I was like, 'Oh my God!' So I went back home and Patti made me an appointment, and we went to the doctor and he said I had bronchitis or pneumonia and gave me some medicine. So, all's good. And how are you?" he said, eager to change the subject.

"I'm fine, and I sure am glad to see that you're all right and that you finally went to see a doctor, John. I've been so worried. We can't lose you, you know. You're the only one with any common sense around here!"

Johnny laughed off the flattering comment with a smile and a chuckle, though that was exactly the kind of thing he lived for.

35

"How's Chester? I haven't seen him lately. What's my head dog been up to?"

"Oh, nothing new. He's just fine. We can't complain," she said about her husband, the head of the three township supervisors who had hired Johnny for the zoning officer position. Chester had settled on the gregarious man when, during the interview, the inspector described his philosophy of "charging extra for stupid." Their friendship strengthened when they discovered they shared a birthday.

"Do you have any zoning stuff I need to take care of today? Bill didn't call, did he?" Johnny asked, certain that he had. He purposefully didn't listen to any of his messages, sure his supervisor had called screaming and dreaded hearing it.

"No, Bill didn't call, but Gabriel Glick left a message looking for you. He said he's called you a couple times and you haven't got back with him."

"Oh God," he sighed heavily to illustrate his exasperation with the pushy Amishman. "He can wait. That guy's nothin' but trouble." Secretly he was relieved to hear that Bill hadn't called Grace and assumed it was a good sign.

"You know what? I shouldn't say that," he corrected. "Gabriel listens to me now, but it's been a struggle. Did I ever tell you about the first time I met him?"

"I don't know, John," she said, though she had. She'd heard all of his stories over and over and never got tired of hearing any of them.

"Oh my God. Listen to this! OK—back when I started in inspections, I was told by Labor and Industry that there was this one Amish guy who was doin' a project up around Strasburg who had tried to bribe one of their inspectors."

"Mr. Glick? That doesn't surprise me."

"Yeah. Well, when you hear things like that, you kinda put it in the back of your memory and you don't let go of it. You know what I mean?"

Grace nodded with the slow blink of having been in that situation many times in her sixty-four years.

"Well, sure enough, he lives here in Bart, and, sure enough, he called up wantin' to meet with me. So I went over to his place and picked him up and we drove over to look at a project. We looked at it and I told him what I could do, this and that, and I drove him back. And when I drove him back to his place to drop him off, he starts to get out and goes, 'Well, John. I need to pay you for your time.' I said, 'No, you don't. I get paid.' He says, 'Oh no. That's not enough.' He reaches in his wallet and starts throwin' hundred-dollar bills at me."

"What? An Amishman throwing hundred-dollar bills?" Grace asked with surprise since The Amish were well known for their frugality.

"Yeah! I know! You don't see that often. So I figure out that this was the guy Labor and Industry warned me about who had tried to bribe them, and, of course, I quickly told him what he could do with his hundred-dollar bills and where he could shove those hundred-dollar bills or I would never help him again, and that he would get on my bad list, and that's a list you don't want to be on!"

"You're daggone right!" Grace said, nodding again.

"Anyway, he put his money back in his wallet and he said, 'Well, I'm just trying to help out,' he said, 'You don't get enough money.' I says, 'What I get is my business, it's not your business.'"

"That man is something else, I tell ya. We sure have some odd ones around here, don't we. I keep sayin', John, you should write a book!"

"Oh! I didn't tell you yet, did I?" he said, his tired eyes sparkling. "My daughter, Audra, is going to help me write one."

"Well, it's about time. I get the first copy!"

***

Completely exhausted from getting in and out of the truck and in and out of the cold at inspection after inspection, Johnny thought hard about going home. He didn't want to deal with Gabriel, and though it was only noon, he just wanted to sit in front of the sports network and sleep. Unfortunately, his well-developed sense of duty got the best of him, and he decided to drop by the Nickel Mines project to see how far they'd come before getting up with the persistent Mr. Glick and calling it a day.

As he rolled up to the soon-to-be four-way stop, even before he pulled into the lot, he spotted Bill Herman. The squat, balding man with a large belly was stomping across the street with purposeful steps and a sour face, coming straight toward him.

"John!" Bill shouted as he got closer to his zoning officer's driver side. "Where have you been? I've been trying to get a hold of you all week!"

Johnny sighed and rolled his eyes on the inside. Determined not to show his great annoyance, he pretended he hadn't heard the man and rolled down the window once he came to a stop. "Hey Bill. How are ya?"

Bill repeated himself giving Johnny time to think. "Listen," the zoning officer said, "I was away on a golfing trip then I came home with pneumonia. This is the first day I've been back. I haven't had time to get through all my messages."

"What is going on?" Bill asked, fire in his eyes. "Why are they digging again? It's been shaking my house. I'm afraid it's going to damage the foundation!"

"Sorry, man," Johnny said calmly despite what he felt, trying to keep it light. "Listen, I might just be a dumb hillbilly, but I know a little something about construction, and I promise ya—a little diggin' iddn't gonna damage your house." Before his father's death, Johnny had worked side by side with him for thirty years in the family drywall business.

Unfortunately, Johnny's cool words failed to extinguish Bill's anger. "If there's any damage to my house, my wife's going to skin me alive. Why is Gabriel Glick digging again?"

"Bill, listen. Just relax," he said in a soothing tone in a vain attempt to calm his irate supervisor. "Gabe's done everything I've asked him to do."

"Gabe?" he said, stressing the nickname. "What, are you best buddies with him now? Are you the one to blame for this?"

He was shocked by the choice of words. Didn't Bill remember giving him free rein to do as he saw fit? Johnny certainly did. A year and a half ago, right after he caught wind that Gabriel Glick had bought the property across from Bill Herman's house, he coincidentally walked into the township building when all three supervisors were there discussing road costs.

"Oh, boys," Johnny started, "since I got you all here together and I know it's going to be a problem," he said and explained the situation, "I need to know what you want done with it."

Bill's eyes lit up and he jumped to answer. "Oh, we want that intersection improved. We want him to tear the building down." Larry, the third supervisor, seconded the opinion while Chester remained silent.

"Blame?" Johnny said, playing dumb. "I don't know what you're talking about."

"It looks like he's building another building! There's only supposed to be one on this lot. Did you tell him he could have two buildings?"

"Bill," Johnny began in his own defense with slow, deliberate words without raising his voice, "you told me I could handle it however I wanted if I could get him to tear down the old building. I got him to tear it down by giving him two, which is what he wanted anyway. Everybody's happy."

"I'm not happy!" Bill insisted, his face getting redder. "He can't have two buildings on this lot!"

"Yes, he can, Bill."

"No he can't, it's illegal!"

After the inspector reiterated that Gabriel was well within the legal limits, quoting the code book, Bill grumbled something under his breath and stomped back to his house across the street in a huff. Suspecting this was only the beginning of Bill's discontent, a horrible thought crossed Johnny's mind: what if Bill got so mad at him for giving the go-ahead for the second building, that he teamed up with Larry, whom the inspector never trusted, and they forced him out of his beloved position as Bart Township's zoning officer? It would be terrible for the Amish and their community. He was their biggest ally. They had prospered enormously since he'd been there. He helped them more than anyone. He solved their problems. He couldn't leave—God himself put him there. He couldn't be ousted… unless… unless his work was done.

***

At his follow-up appointment a few days later, the doctor determined that the pneumonia or bronchitis was clearing up. Johnny described the other issues he'd been having: the severe bloating that kept him from eating much, and the pain in his side that prevented him from laying down to sleep. Tests were scheduled. He didn't bother pointing out the growing lump near his collarbone.

Everyone had their guess: Johnny's mother, Ruth, thought it was gallbladder disease, Audra thought it was stomach cancer (but she thought everything could be cancer), and Patti thought his body chemistry changed and that it was a severe case of indigestion. She saw it on Dr. Phil once.

A few weeks and one inconclusive ultrasound later, the doctor gave him a shot. "If my hunch is right," she said, "this will make you feel like you've eaten a really heavy, greasy meal." The shot felt like a rack of ribs, a Gorilla sundae, and a milkshake to wash it all down. At his next appointment when Johnny reported that the shot had "knocked him out for a couple days," the diagnosis was made. Ruth was right. It was gallbladder disease, or, more specifically, that it wasn't working. The doctor recommended having it removed; Johnny wondered how removing something that was causing problems because it wasn't working would fix anything, but didn't ask any questions and assumed the doctors knew what they were doing.

The surgery was scheduled for a couple Monday mornings from then, easy for him to remember since it was to be exactly a week after the Phillies started their regular season. He looked forward to both with high hopes of good outcomes and tried to put the trouble at Nickel Mines out of his mind.

Standing: Bob Bakalez, R.D. Suits, Frank Parrish (crouching), Dave Huston, Dave Hammer, Duffy Sample
Kneeling: Steve Moran, Johnny Coldiron, Golfing trip to Mountain City, TN, early 90's
(photo courtesy of Dave Huston)

Johnny Coldiron, cir. 1988 (photo courtesy of Dave Huston)

CHAPTER 6

April

Early on the scheduled Monday morning, the surgeon extracted Johnny's gallbladder. That very same afternoon, ignoring the doctor's orders, he plodded by his blooming daffodils, crammed himself into his little pickup truck, and sped away to Amishland. He was invincible and trying hard to ignore the pain.

In fact, he concentrated so hard on ignoring the pain, he couldn't take in the breathtaking springtime beauty of Lancaster county. Green, yellow, white, and pink blossomed on both sides of the roads that twisted and turned along. Identical farms unnaturally close together dotted the graceful hillsides like a double-vision painting. The trees, reflecting the bright sun, sparkled from a brief shower that was sure to make the newly sown corn and tobacco fields, still black with the rich fertile soil, sprout tender green shoots.

He parked in front of the small building with black letters over the garage that spelled out "Bart Municipal Building," and walked through the door.

"John?" Grace gasped with wide eyes in a mix of excitement and terror as if she'd seen a ghost. "What are you doing here?"

"What do you mean?" Johnny said, playing dumb again.

"Didn't you have surgery this morning?" She could hardly believe her zoning officer was standing in front of her. She hadn't expected to see him until next Monday at the earliest.

"I've got to get some work done!" he insisted.

She scolded him, telling him that he needed to rest and that work could wait, but deep down she was impressed.

"I'll rest when I'm dead!" he said, grinning, and only half joking.

"That's what I'm afraid of," she said, only half joking, too, and scolded him again for running around after surgery. She demanded he take it easy, reminding him that he wasn't a "spring chicken" anymore.

"I'm fine! I was up walkin' around before they even wheeled me into the post-op room," he boasted. When she looked at him like he was pulling her leg, he swore it was true and started in on his latest story:

"I'm serious! When I came to, I was on the stretcher in a hallway with a whole bunch of other people on stretchers like we were in some kind of hospital traffic jam. I don't know what was up, maybe they didn't have the room ready or somethin', but I had to go bad. I mean, *real* bad. I told the nurse I had to go and she was like, 'The room is almost ready!' I said, 'Ma'am, you don't understand,' I said, 'If I don't get to a bathroom now you're gonna have a mess to clean up!' So I looked around and saw the door to the men's room just down the hallway and I got off my stretcher—the nurses were yellin' at me to wait—and I rolled the stand with the IV bag still attached to my arm all the way to the men's room with me. When I came out all the nurses were starin' at me and one goes, 'Well, we don't need to ask you if you can stand up!' "

Grace laughed and shook her head in adoration. "Oh, John, I can just see it. You're somethin' else! Well, I sure am glad that you're OK. I don't know what we'd do without you around here."

Johnny chuckled and shuffled his feet, hiding his pain. "Do you have anything for me?" he asked, hoping Bill or Gabriel hadn't called again and wishing that mess at Nickel Mines would just go away.

"As a matter of fact, I do have somethin' for you," she said and reached inside the purse on her desk. "Me and Chester got you a little somethin'." She handed him an envelope and started to tear up. He lifted the unsealed flap and removed the gift certificate to the Bullfrog Inn, a popular restaurant and bar just down the road.

"That's it!" Johnny shouted. "I'm takin' you and Chester there tomorrow!"

"No, now, that's for you and Patti," Grace insisted, wiping her eyes. "You're not allowed to spend it on us!"

"Yeah, we'll see about that," he said, but it was no use. To him gift certificates became opportunities to buy presents for the person who gave it to him, treating him to dinner was nearly impossible even on his birthday, and under no circumstances would he ever, *ever* accept cash for anything other than work, and sometimes not even then.

"Anything you have I need to take care of?" he asked again, this time being more specific. She said she didn't have anything, at least nothing that couldn't wait, and demanded he go home and get some rest.

Johnny limped out the door, keeping up appearances of health and strength, shocked to realize the extent of the exhaustion that had just swallowed him whole, making him doubt if he could even get home without falling asleep at the wheel.

He barely made it to the house and down his brick pathway. Around the corner his dogs greeted him, bouncing on top of each other, whipping their tails side to side with their tongues hanging out. He smiled. After opening the gate, he bent down to pet them and felt a sudden, sharp stabbing pain. *It's nothing. It's just from the surgery. That's to be expected*, he assured himself as he stumbled through the door and sank into his recliner in front of the sports network.

***

Two days later, Johnny stopped at Hometown Builders to see if he missed any new gossip while he'd been healing in his overstuffed chair. He shuffled in, pretending to be all better.

"Hallo John!" Dan said as he sprang up from his computer

44

and leaped over to shake his friend's hand. "Good to see you, old man!"

"Are you feelin' better?" Liz asked from across the open space where she sat writing out checks in the kitchen.

"Are you kiddin' me? I feel like a new man!" He limped around the divide and grabbed her shoulders from behind. "In fact, I feel so good, I think you and me should go back to the house!" he said in jest to get a rise.

Before anyone had a comeback, two older ladies who Johnny didn't recognize, walked in from the back to where he stood. "Oh, John, I need to introduce you-in's," Liz said as she rose from her chair and stepped between the women.

Before she could get the next words out, Johnny said, "Let me guess. These are your sisters." The older ladies gushed and fell all over themselves in flattery.

"This is my mother," Liz said, motioning to the woman on her left, "and this is my step mother-in-law," indicating the woman on her right. They both wore bonnets and blue dresses covered in black aprons, looking nearly identical.

"Nice to meet you both!" he said sweetly; they said the same.

Liz looked to her step mother-in-law and deadpanned, "John here is next in line when Dan dies." The senior ladies slapped their knees and carried on as if that was the best joke they'd heard in a decade. Johnny screamed with laughter. "He's our zoning officer, and he got the medical center put in," she explained.

"Well, I couldn't have done it without Dan over there," Johnny insisted. "He hooked me up with this Amish guy named Dutchie Dave. Now, there's a character. He says there are three things he likes: to play golf, drink wine, and smoke cigars!" The women, amused with the list of decidedly un-Amish pastimes, waited for the rest of the story.

"Last year—or was it a year and half ago—we were tryin' to get the new medical center in here because basically there needed to be another place to have all these daggone Amish babies."

The women giggled.

"Honest to God!" he squealed. "Before we got the medical

center put in, the old birthing center across the road had over 400 births there in one year. Now, if ya notice," he said, lowering his head and grinning at the ladies through his bushy eyebrows, "that's more than one baby a day!" They giggled again.

"So we needed this medical center, and I was havin' a lot of trouble gettin' the project off center with DEP—that's the Department of Environmental Protection—because you need their approval to move a certain amount of dirt. And it was just drivin' me nuts because we needed it to start. And I'm over here one day tellin' Dan about it, and he suggests I get up with this guy, Dutchie Dave.

"So, I get up with Dutchie Dave and tell him my problem, and he says to me, he says, 'John, let me help you out.' I said, 'OK, what idea do you have?' 'Well listen,' he says, 'call my friend Senator Smucker and talk to his secretary, Lisa. They'll take care of ya.' I thought, 'Right. This Amishman is hooked up with these political people. This is gonna be funny.' So anyway, I didn't call—at least not then.

"Now, as time goes on, I was still havin' trouble and something came up, and I had a reason to call Senator Smucker's office. So I'm talkin' to the secretary and I says to her, I said, 'Ma'am, what's your first name?' She said, 'Lisa.' I said, 'Really?' I said, 'Is there any chance you know a guy named Dutchie Dave?' She goes, 'Oh my God, are you kidding me? We love him!' She goes, 'He's Senator Smucker's best friend!' "

The ladies clapped and laughed in delight; Johnny had them in the palm of his hand. "So I explained the problem," he continued, "and she called me twice a day every day for another two weeks until we had DEP approval. Dutchie Dave was hooked up politically, unbelievably!

"Now, at the same time, I was doing another job in another township for a family—a huge house, like a million, million and a half dollar house—I'm doing the inspections on it, and this guy, a past political person named Gib Armstrong, owned it. So this kid who worked for him was there and I said to him—because I didn't know anything else to talk about—I said to him, 'It's really funny,' I said, 'I got hooked up politically by an Amishman.' And the boy

46

looks at me and he goes, 'It wouldn't have been Dutchie Dave, would it? He's Gib Armstrong's favorite guy!' I'm like, 'Oh, you've got to be kiddin' me. This is unreal!' " Johnny threw his head back and laughed and laughed at the memory. The ladies were equally entertained by the story and storyteller himself.

"Is this the one you wanted me to remind you to tell? It was something about the medical center," Liz asked.

Johnny scrunched up his face and turned his head to the side, while still squinting at the questioner, trying to remember. "Oh!" he said, "No, that's another one with my engineer, Derrick, but that's what happened next." Without missing another beat, he launched into that one:

"So anyway, after all that, we were havin' trouble gettin' the plans through County. My engineer, Derrick, called me up and asked me to go up there with him for a meeting. He said, 'John, you can talk to them better than I can.' So I met him there and I said, 'What's the problem?' They said, 'Well, we think this new project should have sidewalks and...' I said, 'Sidewalks?' I said, 'Are you kidding me?' I said, 'There are no other sidewalks around. I've got enough six-year-old kids pullin' wagons on 896 as is!' I says, 'And you're gonna dump more out? It ain't happenin' in my lifetime!' I said, 'Now we're here and we're makin' all decisions today. There will be no other discussions when we leave here, so let's make them, but there's no sidewalks. Next?'

"The county girl went, 'Well, couldn't we do something? Like, maybe a little walking trail?' I said, 'Oh! That's easy.' I said, 'Derrick.' " He reenacted by pointing to the left, " 'Put a little pavement walking trail around the project. People can walk around it. That's fine.' Derrick goes, 'OK, yeah.' I said, 'Next.' She goes, 'Oh,' " Johnny said meekly, imitating her voice the way he remembered it, " 'well, I guess that's all.' 'OK,' I said, 'we're done! We're outta here. I consider this project over. See ya!' "

The ladies laughed and giggled and waited for more.

"Oh yeah!" he said smiling, soaking up the attention. "I learned early on when we rebuilt the school house that you don't have to pay any attention to County. You have to tell *them* what to do.

"So anyway, we walk out of the County building and Derrick goes, 'You see why I took you to that meeting?' I says, 'I knew why I was there,' I says, 'Got what we wanted, didn't we?' He's like, 'Yep. Thank you very much!' " Johnny exclaimed proudly, nodding with his hands in his pockets, shuffling his stance and laughing.

"And the funny part was," he said, starting to laugh louder at his favorite upcoming part, "when Derrick first got there, he asked me, he says, 'Where'd you park?' I said, 'I parked right along the street.' He goes, 'Where? There was no parking. I had to park back here,'—behind the county building—'and I think I'm going to get a ticket!' I said, 'I parked in a no parking zone.' He looks at me like I'm crazy. I say to him, I says, 'You think they've got the nerve to put a ticket on a truck with a light on top?' " Johnny laughed again and made sure the ladies were still hanging on his every word.

"So Derrick calls me after the meeting and he goes, 'Yup. I was right. I got a ticket. Did you?' I said, 'Heck, no, I didn't get a ticket,' " he said proudly, then paused for the punchline: "Could I interest you in a yellow truck with a light on top?"

Dan jumped into the room just now remembering something he wanted to tell Johnny, interrupting the laughter.

"Oh, John, I heard that Bill was pretty upset about the concrete that was poured up at Nickel Mines."

"What?" Johnny said, his pulse quickening. "I hadn't heard that. How did you hear this?"

"Mose said one of his guys said that he came out of his house screamin' that it woke him up. It was really early in the mornin', somethin' like 4:00 am."

"Oh man. Oh, that's not good," he said, his heart racing, and his brows moving closer together. "That's not good at all. I need to go see Grace." He rushed out the door and sped out of the parking lot, cutting off a buggy, and was out of his truck in front of the township building in minutes.

He burst through the door in a near panic, trying to appear cool. "Grace!" he shouted as he walked as quickly as he could to her desk. "I was just over at Hometown Building. I heard Bill went nuts this morning when the concrete was poured at Nickel Mines. Is that true?"

Grace nodded and confirmed that Mr. Herman had called that morning and wasn't very happy. He had demanded that she get up with the solicitor and have him send Gabriel Glick a cease-and-desist letter until the matter was cleared up, insisting that the proposed uses for the buildings were in violation of the zoning ordinance. In addition, now that there was another building going up, he no longer considered the project completed, and operating a business before completion was also a violation.

"Personally I think he's just mad at being woken up. And you know he doesn't like Mr. Glick," Grace said. "It wouldn't surprise me if he was just lookin' for a way to get him in trouble."

Johnny convinced himself that Bill wanted to get *him* in trouble, too. He was probably teaming up with Larry right now to conspire against him.

"So is that all he said?" Johnny questioned, really wanting to ask if his name had come up but didn't want to appear paranoid.

"Well, he just said that after I get up with the solicitor and Mr. Glick gets the cease-and-desist letter, we'll decide on whether or not to reinstate the permits at the next supervisor meeting, and whether or not to schedule a zoning hearing for its uses."

Johnny didn't want to believe his ears, sure that Bill was blaming him. Bill had said exactly that when he ran into him a few weeks ago, but he had never told Grace about it. He limped out the door in a daze, heading into a tailspin of despair, when he saw Chester pull in the gravel parking lot.

Johnny shook hands with the tall, thin, white haired man. He then filled him in about the cease-and-desist letter, reminding the supervisor of the day he had walked into the township building when he and the other two supervisors there conducting business.

"I don't know what he expected," Chester said, shaking his head. "I told him, 'It's John Coldiron. If you tell him to do what he wants, he's going to do what he thinks is right.' "

Johnny felt better after hearing his head supervisor say that, but hinted at his growing fear that Bill would team up with Larry and force him out as zoning officer.

"Not if I have anything to do with it," Chester said, assuring his friend that it was likely not a big deal and not to worry about it. He theorized that Bill's wife had gotten upset about her new, clear view about to be obstructed again with the second building, and had pressured Bill to do something about it.

Johnny didn't know what to think. Suddenly it seemed like everything was going wrong. Even the Phillies were having their worst season ever. What could possibly be next? A sharp pain in his side almost took his breath away. He crossed a few more names off his list and went home in a decidedly grumpy mood.

Bart Township Building

CHAPTER 7

Early May

For a few more weeks as the irises and lilies by the path to his apartment formed their buds, Johnny continued to wince through his inspections; the pain that he had expected to get better was only getting worse. One morning he visited his mother, who noticed the excruciating pain he tried to mask while forcing down his biscuits and gravy. "Now, Johnny, this ain't natural. You need to call the doctor!" she said. The words rang in his ears all weekend. Finally, when Patti noticed that he couldn't even talk due to clenching his teeth so hard in response to his pain, like it or not, she scheduled an appointment for him the next day.

The doctor, baffled at the pain he was still experiencing, ordered more tests. The ultrasound and x-ray left the doctor guessing at the cause of his intense discomfort and ordered another higher resolution CT scan for the following week.

Tuesday arrived with another appointment and the results of the latest test. *Nothing could be found with all the other tests*, Johnny thought, *so why do they keep looking?* He thought the inconclusive tests were a waste of time and money. *If these last ones come up with nothing, I'm not going to have any more*, he thought. *I'm done.*

After what seemed like an unusually long wait, the doctor finally came in to where the couple sat. This time she had news.

"We found nodules internally, in the lungs, and on the breastbone," she said matter-of-factly. "It could be anything from dust particles to scars. A biopsy will be needed to determine exactly what it is."

"OK... When can that be done?" Johnny asked eagerly, ready to get all this medical stuff over with and back to his normal life.

The doctor scheduled his biopsy for Thursday at 10:30 am, and instructed the patient to be at the hospital two hours before the appointed time to check in and get prepped for surgery.

***

Johnny and Patti arrived at the hospital ten minutes before 8:30 am on Thursday. As usual, Johnny conducted business the entire way.

"You know that call I just got off of?" he said to his wife as she drove them in her little, orange Ford Focus. "Well, that same Amish guy called me up, like, a year ago, and he goes, 'John, can you come up? I've got a problem.' I said, 'OK.' I get up there and I say, 'What's the problem, Zeek?' He goes, 'Well, in our church we have a lady who's being abused by her husband, and we got to get her away from him.' He says, 'I'd like to put her in a trailer up here on my son's property.' I said, 'OK, I can help out.'

"Then I said, 'Zeek. Is this your daughter?' He looks at me and says, 'Yeah.' I said, 'Well, Zeek, there's solutions to this.' 'I know,' he says. 'John, do you think you could get some of your hillbilly relatives to come up here and beat the ever-livin' shit outta him?'" Johnny cackled at the comment.

"And... and, see," he said, still laughing, "Amishmen *never* cuss. And I said, 'Yeah, I could, Zeek, but I think you should do it yourself!' I said, 'I'll tell you right now, if somebody did that to my daughter, he'd be looking at the bad side of a baseball bat!'"

"Johnny!" Patti scolded.

"It's the truth!" he squealed. "And Zeek goes, 'He's just a little weasel.' He was a little short guy, and I said, 'Well, it'd be all that easier to kick his butt!' I said, 'My goodness, that'd be fun!'" Johnny laughed and laughed and sighed, repeating his favorite part:

"He said, 'Can you get some of your hillbilly relatives?' I love it!'"

It was because of his hillbilly relatives that he felt such a kinship with the Amish. His parents grew up in the hills of North Carolina without electricity or cars. Their formal education was in a one-room schoolhouse that, like the Amish ones, only went up to the eighth grade. After that, if you didn't go to high school an hour away —and few did—you were expected to work in the fields or learn a trade if you hadn't already. The inspector had recently kidded with one of Bart's other bishops: "I finally agree with what has been said. God did put me here for a reason," he told the man, setting up the punchline and deliberately dumbing down his grammar: "It was because I don't fit nowhere else!"

Patti pulled up to the hospital entrance and let Johnny out. He tried to look completely normal while walking in so that they'd be surprised when they realized he was having surgery. He didn't look sick. Even though he'd lost forty pounds, he could stand to lose at least forty or sixty more. He signed in and sat in the waiting room, another doctor's office that looked just like the last. Patti eventually sat across from him while he checked his messages: five from various Amishmen with questions about permits including a favorite bishop in Buck (a neighboring county) whose Amish son was an electrician, one English who wanted to complain about a neighbor, and one from Mose who said the plans were done and he could pick them up. The only message he had interest in returning at that moment was Mose's, but he couldn't just call and get him. Like all Amishmen, you had to leave a message and wait until he called back. Johnny figured he'd be done and out of there by that time.

A nurse ushered the couple into another room where she took the patient's vitals and gave him a gown to change into. He laid on a gurney as instructed while the nurse hooked him up to an IV to prepare him for surgery. He was glad he was scheduled for the morning so he could get to some work in the afternoon.

Fifteen minutes before his scheduled time in the operating room, the nurse came in. "I'm so sorry, Mr. Coldiron, a heart attack victim came in and we'll have to bump you back a couple of hours."

"Not a problem!" he said cheerfully though that was not how

he felt. *Hopefully the surgery itself won't take too long,* he thought. *What the heck am I going to do for two hours?*

He flirted with the nurses who came in, and told them stories about the Amish. More time passed. He picked up his phone and called his son to see if he could possibly do some inspections for him that he had originally thought he'd get to that day. He didn't answer. He called Grace to see if anything pressing came up that he needed to take care of. There wasn't. When he couldn't think of anybody else to call, and his phone was almost dead with his charger in his truck at home, he looked over at his wife, her eyes glued to her phone.

A nurse walked in. He straightened up in the bed, ready to get the show on the road. Bad news again: another emergency and it might be another four hours this time. They both sighed and groaned. The nurse suggested to Patti that she go to lunch so she immediately sprang from her chair and asked her husband if she wanted her to bring him anything. The nurse reminded her that he couldn't eat before surgery.

"Can you bring me my phone charger?" Johnny asked. "It's in my truck."

"I wasn't going to go home. I don't want to miss them wheeling you in."

"They said it might be four hours."

"What if they're wrong?"

He sighed. "OK. Whatever."

Patti shuffled out the door without saying goodbye, glad to be released, if just for a few hours. Irritated, Johnny closed his lids to "rest his eyes." When, in a few hours he opened them again, Patti was sitting beside him playing on her phone and his phone charger lay on top of the blanket that covered his belly. He charged his phone and listened to his messages: a couple more calls from the same Amishmen with questions about their permits. He tried to call his son again.

"Hello?"

"Hey. Can you do a couple inspections for me today?"

"I don't know."

The vague answer rubbed Johnny the wrong way. *Why can't he just be happy to help?* "Well, I'm in the hospital and can't get to them."

"You're still in the hospital?"

"Yeah," Johnny said, now more irritated than before and asked him again if he could do the inspections or not.

"Uh… Yeah. OK," Young John said like it wasn't exactly a chore, but it wasn't his first choice of things to do either.

"Thanks." Johnny told him the specifics and after hanging up half muttered to himself, "Geez. Why does everything have to be a struggle with him?" He could just picture his son playing video games on their big TV on the wall, wasting a perfectly nice, sunny day when he should be working, or at least be outside getting something done around the house. Patti looked up but didn't bother answering.

A couple nurses came in, and he told a couple more stories, lightening his mood. Still, the wait was killing him. He didn't want to think about the "what ifs." Finally, at the end of the day, the nurses administered the anesthesia and wheeled Johnny down the long hall to the operating room. His bloodshot blue eyes closed.

After the surgery the nurses wheeled him into a post-op room. For a few moments after regaining consciousness, he felt disoriented and he didn't know where he was. When his eyelids finally lifted and he saw his wife standing above him, peering into his bleary eyes, he remembered his location. He could tell by the look on her face that something was terribly wrong. He hoped to God she wasn't going to tell him what, deep down, he already knew.

"Where's the doc?" he asked, scanning the room, still unable to focus clearly.

"She left," Patti answered, looking like she was going to say more but couldn't get the words out. After the surgery the doctor hurried to go, not bothering to offer an explanation. On her way out, she dryly gave Patti the results to relay to her husband.

Johnny said nothing and waited for her to say something, anything. Patti swallowed hard. Why did she have to tell him? Why couldn't the doctor have stayed for fifteen more minutes? Time stood still.

"It's cancer," he heard her say as if she were reciting a line in a play. The words echoed inside his skull. "They found cancer in your lungs and on your breast bone. Lung cancer." Patti swayed and looked as if she might faint. She put her hand over her already weakened heart.

Johnny tried to sit up to hold her steady, but couldn't. The room still spun from the drugs, and he hoped he'd misheard her. She repeated the dreadful news she never wanted to deliver in the first place. It sank in that his deepest fear had come true: it was The Big C.

The Big C: the otherwise innocuous third letter of the alphabet that, when prefixed correctly, can spark panic and terror in otherwise happy and unassuming people who are just going about the routine of their lives.

He spouted off the prepared speech that he had hoped he wouldn't have to give, like a candidate who lost an election. "Well, they must have caught it early if they couldn't even find it until now. It's nothing. Don't worry about a thing. They caught it early. I'm sure they did. We'll work on it. You'll see. This is nothin'."

Patti's green eyes glazed over and became unfocused. "It never crossed my mind that it could be cancer," she said in a distant voice, so sad that tears wouldn't even fall.

"Look," he tried hard to reassure her in a calm, steady voice, "you'll go on your trip tomorrow, and when you come back, we'll find out it was no big deal after all."

"The trip?" Patti asked, like she had forgotten all about it, the devastating news superseding everything that had come before it. "I can't go now!" Suddenly leaving was unthinkable, as unthinkable as *not* going had been hours before.

"Yes you can, Patti," Johnny insisted sharply, as if she were just being stubborn. "You have to go. I'm taking you to the airport tomorrow, and that's all there is to it."

"No, Johnny!" she shouted like a child bucking punishment. "I'm not going, OK?" Her sparse but neat brows nearly touched. She couldn't think of abandoning her husband in his greatest hour of need. "I don't want to go!" She leaned over and they embraced, tears mixing, hearts still beating.

"It will all be OK, Patti," he said between her sniffles. "Don't worry. Everything's going to be fine."

When they got home to their basement apartment, they did what should never be done: they looked up survival rates for lung cancer. With the help of their son, Young John, who, along with his wife and five children, lived upstairs from them, the threesome crowded around the computer screen in the kitchen. It wasn't good. According to the American Lung Association at www.lung.org, "More than half of people with lung cancer die within one year of being diagnosed." Johnny wouldn't accept it. He would be the exception, he was sure of it. He always was. He would beat it.

Patti started having chest pains.

Johnny staggered down the steep staircase to his basement apartment with a resolve bordering on delusional. *I'm going to beat it; those statistics don't apply to me; I'm different, special.* He turned on the sports network and collapsed into his recliner. *Tomorrow I'll spread the word*, he thought. Even before his eyes completely closed, he slipped into unconsciousness for the night.

CHAPTER 8

May 19, Penn Medical Center

Tuesday morning Johnny limped his way across his living room past his wife to greet his daughter, Audra, with a big hug. She had arrived at their basement apartment to accompany her parents to their 8:00 am appointment with the oncologist where they would learn the full diagnosis.

"Thanks for comin', little girl," he said, feeling kind of bad that she drove three hours just for him. "It really means a lot to your mother." Patti had taken the news especially hard and started back on her anti-anxiety medication. "Ah. There's Dolly!" he said, spotting his youngest child, a high school history teacher who had asked off for the day to attend the appointment as well. "OK. Let's go!"

Johnny, his wife, and two of his four children piled into Dolly's Range Rover. Patti took the passenger seat while Audra sat in back beside her father with the tape recorder between them in case he told any Amish stories on the way that she could use for the book he wanted her to help him with.

"Our friends have been just wonderful," Patti said, sporting her new hair cut she got that weekend to console herself. Dolly started the engine. "Cheryl—you know Cheryl, right? Dave Huston's wife? She organized a spontaneous dinner party on Saturday with everybody. Everyone's being so nice."

"Oh yeah. Everybody up in Bart, too," Johnny added. "I tell ya, the area I work in is so funny. Yesterday I go to Worth's used car lot—and it's one of the nicest businesses, English businesses, in Bart —and they were wantin' a permit. I'd already given them a couple permits, but they were sellin' their farm that was the home place of Milton Hershey, where he grew up, so we thought it was gonna bring a lot of money-"

"You mean, as in Hershey Chocolate?" Audra asked.

"Yeah. So we thought it was gonna bring a lot of money, and I wanted to know what happened at the auction on Saturday so I drop in, and I look over and they are diggin' the addition on the house next to their business that I hadn't permitted yet. But I told 'em to go ahead, it was no big deal and I'd get to it," Johnny said, adjusting himself in the backseat. "So anyway, they told me the farm didn't bring as much as they thought, but they went ahead and sold it. An Amish family bought it, and, see, to me that was just awful because the Amish'll just gut it even though it's historical. They might even tear the house down. And he said, 'Oh, we're building the addition, John. You told me it was OK!' I said, 'Yeah,' I said, 'No big deal.' I said, 'I'll walk over there and look at the footers,' I said, 'Just calm down. Everything's fine!' " Johnny laughed remembering the situation.

"I said, 'I'm more worried about your mom'—because she's been sick—'and you sellin' the farm and everything like that. I've got other issues I need to work on.' I said, 'I was just diagnosed Thursday night with some lung cancer.'

"And within a matter of seconds I'm in prayer service. I mean, Mrs. Bandy takes me in her office and is praying to God that he lay hands on me for, like, forty-five minutes! It's just... I mean, it was just beautiful. And, of course, she gets done and she's got to hug me and, of course, I think, 'Where else in the world would those kinds of things happen?' And, of course, they are there and they are almost cryin' and they're sayin', 'John, we love you!' " "

"Wait, this isn't an Amish family?" Audra confirmed.

"No. They're Mennonite—which is close enough." It is

common for those who leave the Amish church—and those who choose to never join at all—to become Mennonite. However, like the Amish, the Old Order Mennonite women in Lancaster County still wear bonnets and plain dresses, but the men are not required to wear beards, straw hats, or suspenders.

"Anyway, I'm like, 'Geez!' It's just a different atmosphere up there. It's nothing like around where we live because our area is all... it's all built up now." He paused but before anyone else could say anything, he went on again.

"I went over to Hometown Builders and told Dan and them over there, then went through to the restaurant side and told the owner, Abe, because he's my buddy, too. I'm sure they've told everybody by now. They were all like, 'John, we'll be prayin' for ya!' Same thing when I sat down with Amos King for a while—he was the one who held the classes in his garage after the school was torn down. They're all waitin' for me to have this meeting with the oncologist so I can come back and let them know more because they are all very, very concerned.

"Then I went and saw Antique because I figured I better tell him because he'll be mad if he hears it through the grapevine and it doesn't come straight from me. And he had, of course, a different perspective on it. He has another person in his church who was just diagnosed with lung cancer, too—and they don't mince any words—he goes, 'Well, she's level four,' and I'm like, 'Oh, God, I hope I'm not level four,' " Johnny laughed nervously and continued on. "And he goes, 'I guess you can't breathe, right?' I says, 'No, I can breathe perfect, deep breaths, I'm fine!' He goes, 'Oh, well, maybe you're not as bad off as her,' and I'm thinkin', 'That would be a nice thing!'

"And then he says, he goes, 'Well, John, you know you were put here for a reason. Maybe God's done with you!' " Johnny roared as if that was the funniest thing he'd ever heard. His family protested. "And I'm laughin' with him, but that's just their culture."

"My God's not done with you!" Audra said.

Johnny chuckled. "Well, maybe that's true. I'm hopin', because I've still got some stuff I want to do. It's just...," he paused and sighed heavily. "It is what it is." He paused again for a few beats, deep in thought.

"It's like when Brooke called me, and she says to me, she says, 'Dad, aren't you scared?' I says, 'Well, no, I can't say I'm scared. It just is what it is. I've got to work on it is all.' "

"Brooke actually called you?" Audra asked, her eyebrows raised.

"Yeah, yeah. I was pretty surprised," he affirmed with several vigorous nods. "So... it just is what it is. It will be interesting. I hope... I hope... but I really don't think we're gonna find out a lot today. That's what I... I wish we'd really find out a lot, set up chemo and be like, 'This is what we're going to do and this is what we're going to do,' " he said, pointing one way then the other. "But I don't think that's gonna be the way. I'm just hoping for the best case scenario where they'd say, 'We got it early so this is the procedure for taking it on early.' That would be wonderful."

Dolly spoke up from the driver seat: "I don't want you to get your hopes up, though, Dad."

"Oh, no, no," he responded quickly, not wanting to appear unrealistic. "It just is what it is."

"It sounds like they found cancer in the bone," she pointed out gingerly.

"Well, that's one of the questions I have. They saw nodules and that mass here," he said, laying his hand over the spot near his collarbone that had doubled to the full size of a mini-marshmallow. "Is this actually on the bone or is it a mass? Uh... what is it? That kind of thing. There's a lot that I want to do. I want to get down to your house," he said, gesturing to his daughter beside him, "I want to play golf, I want to be there for-"

"But, Dad, aren't you feeling great?" Dolly interrupted.

"Yeah, but those are the kinds of things I want to know from him. Can I do? Am I hurting anything by doing? Uh... what am I hurting by playing golf?"

"I wouldn't think you'd be hurting anything," Audra said from experience.

"Well, that's the kind of things though..." He trailed off and looked out the window.

"But, come on, Dad," Audra said, "let's be honest. If they said you were going to hurt something by doing, you'd do it anyway."

"Well, no, no, no. Uh-uh," he insisted, shaking his head in protest. "If he tells me today… if he tells me today that my life will be longer if I never play golf again, then OK. Fine. That's it. I played my last round last week. I've got no problem with that."

"Well, the main problem with you is," Patti spoke up from the front seat, "after the surgery, if you would do what they say, you might feel better."

"What surgery?" Johnny asked like that possibility hadn't crossed his mind. Audra told him they would probably remove the tumors the way they had removed the one from her brain. Patti reminded him of his nephew, Nathan, and the surgeries to remove his cancerous lymph nodes from his melanoma.

"Oh yeah, and I went over to tell Mom and, of course, she took it hard." He didn't want to mention how she sobbed like her heart was being ripped out and begged for him to "get back in church!" "Then while I was there tellin' her, Brenda came over," he said, referring to his younger sister, "and she was like, 'Maybe it's from all the asbestos you removed or mixing up all those drywall buckets and-' "

"Yeah. That's what I think, too," Patti cut in.

"Yeah, it could be," he said, but didn't really agree. "And then she goes, 'Or it could be from sitting next to Dad for thirty years and breathin' in all his secondhand smoke,' and I was like, 'Well, if that's the case, I wouldn't change that for the world.' " He paused a moment as the day he found his father sprawled out on the kitchen floor flashed across his mind. Johnny had come over for coffee that morning when his mother was away visiting relatives. His father had suffered a massive stroke and died a few days later at sixty-five.

"Then Brenda started namin' off these cousins and uncles that have had lung cancer and this and that, and they were all heavy smokers."

"But Dad, you don't smoke!" said Dolly.

"Yeah, I know. That's what your Mamaw said, too. Oh, and I went by and told Grace, my secretary. And, of course, she took it about as well as Mom did. I just gave her a big hug and told her, I said, 'A lot of other people are much worse off than me.' " He sighed and stared straight ahead. "It just is what it is."

All were silent for a moment then Johnny began to chuckle.

"Oh," he said, remembering what his eight-year-old grandson had said when he learned of his ailment, "Zander said the cutest thing to me, though. He said, 'Granddad, if you die I'll pick you the prettiest flowers!' "

"Awww!" was heard from all around the Range Rover.

"Yeah, wasn't that cute? Of course, John hears him say it and he tears into him goin', 'Zander, don't say things like that! We don't talk about it!' I'm thinkin', 'Heck yeah, we're gonna talk about it!' " He chuckled awkwardly.

"I just...," Johnny started again and trailed off, gazing out the window to collect his thoughts. "There's so many questions that I just can't believe that all of them can be answered today and I wonder how long this whole thing will be."

Patti worried aloud that they wouldn't get to the appointment in time. Johnny explained the actual appointment was for 8:45 am, but they wanted you to be there a half an hour early, which eased her mind slightly. It wasn't long before Johnny's mind wandered back to Bart.

"My gut feeling is that I will be worked beyond belief for the next six months with Amish wantin' permits," he said, then laughed in an oddly defeated way.

"Why?" Audra asked. "Why in the next six months?"

"Because, they will want their permits before I die!" he said and laughed again. "I've had 'em say that already!" He let out a sigh and crossed his arms. "Oh, it's all about them. I understand. It's their culture. They've been raised that way. But yesterday I went in to get a burger at the restaurant, and the daughter of the builder, my buddy Dan Stoltzfus who half owns the place, saw me—and she's probably about eighteen or nineteen years old—and I know her had dad told the family because she comes up next to me and says, 'John, are you feelin' OK?' 'Yeah, I'm fine.' So, she knew. So the word's goin' through the grapevine. And let me tell you, the Amish church is the biggest grapevine on the planet. Everybody I tell says, 'We'll pray for ya, John. We'll pray.' Yeah. So everybody's real concerned."

***

The Range Rover pulled into the destination right on time and the foursome filed into the main waiting room. After checking in, the receptionist directed them to another waiting room where Johnny spotted the coffee station and paused there to pour himself a cup while the women found chairs and sat down. *What if it wasn't caught early?* he accidentally thought but quickly reminded himself that he could breathe just fine, so it must have been. Antique's church member could barely breathe with her lung cancer and she was stage four. He sighed and walked over toward his family talking about the color of Audra's sweater that she had borrowed from Mamaw. He sipped his coffee and sat down in the chair, re-adjusting himself a few times as if he didn't quite fit.

"Are you OK, Dad?" Dolly asked, noticing his uncomfortable fidgeting.

"Yeah, yeah, I'm fine, I'm fine. I just hope they tell us they caught it early, that's all."

"That's what we all hope, Dad," Audra said. The women agreed.

"Johnny Coldiron?" A nurse with a clipboard said just loudly enough to hear across the room.

"Here!" he said, shooting up from the chair like a contestant on The Price is Right. The family followed the nurse to the room where, in a few short minutes, the doctor would deliver the news. The nurse took his vitals, asked a few questions, and typed the answers into the tiny laptop on the counter. After she left, they sat in silence, arms crossed, hands wringing, and waited for the door to open again.

After an excruciating few minutes, Dr. Caruso, a short, slender man who looked like he only started shaving sometime in the

64

current president's administration, walked in and introduced himself. He sat on the roller stool by the laptop on the counter. In his calm, quiet voice, he got straight down to business. Johnny's heart pounded.

"I don't have the full pathology in front of me because it's not in yet. I will have it on Thursday. Everything I'm going to tell you today is based on the information I have now. But if the complete report changes things, then what I tell you today might change, and the treatment plan I give you today might change, OK?" He looked to everyone for confirmation. When they all agreed, he continued.

"Again, what we find out on Thursday might change things, but because of your enlarged prostate," Johnny's eyes widened at that discovery, "I'm confident that what we're dealing with here is prostate cancer."

At the news Johnny nearly jumped out of his seat with joy. Patti's hand sprang to her heart and she gasped in relief. "Oh, thank goodness!"

"Oh, yeah!" Johnny shouted like he'd single-handedly won the world series. "That's a lot better than what we thought it was. We were told it was lung cancer. I've had buddies with lung cancer and they just don't make it very long. I've got another one with prostate cancer, and he's had it for, like, fifteen years. Oh, this is nothin'!" Johnny said relieved, feeling like he already escaped death.

Dr. Caruso waited for the brief celebration to end before beginning again.

"It's stage four," the doctor spoke slowly, "having metastasized to your lungs and bones." Patti and Johnny, who were so relieved it wasn't lung cancer, didn't quite grasp the gravity of those words. He went on to list all the places they'd found tumors in his body: lungs, ribs, chest, skull, and spelled out the treatment plan that included testosterone lowering shots, bone strengthening pills, white blood cell boosting shots, and six hour-long intravenous chemotherapy sessions every three weeks.

According to the doctor, five years ago the treatment would have been to take the hormone lowering shots and if that had no effect, to start chemo. However, based on new research, the current treatment started the patient on everything all at once.

"I got it," Johnny said. "That's so the Bad Guys can't get a chance to take over even more!"

Dr. Caruso smiled slightly at the characterization and went on to discuss the specifics about the medications, stressing that while on the bone strengthening medication he couldn't have any dental work done, so before he could take it, he needed to visit a dentist. Johnny told the doctor one of his golfing buddies was a great dentist. When the chemo was mentioned, Johnny said he wanted to get a port like one of his best golfing buddies, Huston, had installed, and showed off his own vein-free arms.

"Now let's address the elephant in the room," Dr. Caruso said, sitting back on his roller stool by the door. "Some people want to know the prognosis, some don't."

"Oh, we want to know!" Johnny said eagerly, speaking for everyone else in the room.

"OK," he said, looking directly at his patient, and paused to carefully gather his words. "I'd say you have... years."

"Oh, thank goodness!" Patti cried again.

"Oh, yeah. That's great! That's great! Oh!" Johnny laughed and doubled over in his chair, smiling big. "See, I'm sixty-three right now, and my dad died at sixty-five of a massive stroke, and I was like, 'Geez, I at least want to live as long as my dad did!' Johnny took a deep breath and sighed in relief.

Dr. Caruso smiled almost imperceptibly and asked if anyone had any questions.

"Well, Doc, I want to know if I'm hurtin' anything by playin' golf."

"No."

"Because if I am, I've played my last round last week!" he insisted with his eyebrows raised and forehead crinkled.

"No, play as much golf as you want."

"See, we told you, Dad," Dolly said.

"Well, I'm just making sure!"

"Let me ask you this," the doctor said to his patient. "How do you *feel*?"

Johnny bounced in his chair with bright eyes to illustrate his answer: "I feel great!"

"As long as you feel good, you can do anything you want to do."

That was exactly what his tired ears wanted to hear. It wasn't going to stop him from living.

When all questions were asked and answered, a nurse led the Coldirons to another, larger room where the chemo would be administered in a few days. Johnny was directed to sit in one of the olive green, vinyl stuffed arm chairs with IV stands and electronic monitors, flanked by smaller armless chairs where his wife and two daughters sat.

A nurse on a stool rolled over to the family in the corner, pulling herself forward with the heels of her sneakers like a crab. As she went over the treatment list again, the overwhelmed patient's internal monologue was so deafening he barely heard her enthusiastically assuring them that they were in good hands, that the facility was excellent, and Dr. Caruso was wonderful.

I have cancer. I really have cancer. Stage four. I'm going to beat it just like Huston did. His was stage four and that was five years ago. Now he's better than ever and havin' the time of his life with a new wife. Everybody's prayin' for me: the Amish, everybody. I can't die. My work isn't done. I'm gonna beat this.

Johnny, Patti, Dolly, and Audra waiting for the doctor.

Johnny waiting for the nurse to give the treatment plan details.

CHAPTER 9

May 19, Amishland

On the ride back, Johnny updated all his friends and family not present with the new diagnosis, spinning it in the best possible light: "Yeah, so this is much better!" and "We can work with this!"

Dolly dropped everybody off at her brother's house and went home. Patti walked down the brick pathway to their basement apartment while Johnny removed a circular saw, a 2x4 scrap, and a tool box from the passenger seat of his truck to make room for Audra. She set a tape recorder, antique technology in 2015, on top of the giant paper stack between the two seats and slipped a blank cassette tape in. She was coming to Amishland with him and wanted to record everything.

Almost as soon as he took off, his phone rang. "Hey Frankie!" he screamed his greeting. Frank responded with concern, knowing his appointment had been that morning.

"Yeah, well, it turns out it's not lung cancer, it's… it's…," he stammered and looked to his passenger.

"Prostate cancer," Audra reminded him.

"Prostate cancer, so that's better than we thought… Yeah, well the doctor—this young guy—said first thing, 'Listen, there's no cure, we just have to stop it from spreading.' They're basically going for chemo throughout my body … Yeah, it will be in a port and go through everything. He said that those bones where the cancer has spread to could be weakened but they'll give me medicine which should strengthen the bone… Yeah… Right. In other words he said, as far as he's concerned he's giving me a prognosis that was much better than coming in there and him telling me I have lung cancer… Yeah… Now, it is considered stage four because any cancer that has went out and spread into other areas automatically gets classified as stage four… Right, but it is stage four in a manner that we can control that stage… Uh-huh… I told him I got a dear buddy that had colon cancer and he's still around doin' good, and I got a buddy who is 85 years old who's got prostate cancer, but the one buddy that had lung cancer is gone, so I feel like this is pretty good news!" He chuckled a little and wound down the conversation. "So, that's the scoop! You're the only one other than my mom who I've told. I haven't been able to get Huston or Cheryl, but if you talk to 'em you can tell 'em everything I know, alright?"

Frank had more questions.

"Yeah, we're gonna do chemo. I gotta see 'em on Friday. That's gonna be a long day. Boy, this doctor stuff is gonna get me… Yeah, yeah, I know, I'm going to make it a priority… Well, I asked him, I said, 'What are my restrictions? Because the boys are gonna wanna know!' And he said, 'No, no, no, no, you listen here,' he said, 'You play golf every chance you get!' Johnny paused to chuckle at the memory he didn't know he paraphrased. "So I said, 'That's good, but what about work?' He said, 'How do you feel?' … Huh? … Yeah… No, I told him 'I feel good.' He goes, 'That's the only thing important, then.' So he said, 'Keep goin'.' ' "

They were halfway to Amishland when he hung up. "That was Frank. I think that really picked his spirits up," Johnny said proudly. "I called him yesterday to let him know we were goin' and you and Dolly were comin' with me and your mom, and he was like, 'If something happens and they can't go, I'll go! I'll go! I'm like, 'Calm down. Everything's gonna be fine.' He was really upset. I don't think I'd ever seen him upset like that."

He dodged a buggy then looked down at his list of things to do that day peeking out from underneath the tape recorder. Audra moved her machine over as he wrote numbers down next to the names in order of importance.

At each inspection, whether he knew the people well or not, he told them of his diagnosis that morning. The first couple times he spread the news he couldn't even remember the name of his specific type of cancer. "What is it again, Audra?" "Prostate," she'd say. Everyone promised to pray.

One inspection of a hot and stuffy addition above a garage in an old two-story house near the road reminded him of the day he finally went to the doctor. "It was a place just like this in Peach Bottom, before all this happened when I got to the top of the steps and couldn't breathe. It was like there was no air." On the way back down, Audra snapped a picture of the coats and straw hats hanging by the door.

Back in the truck, they sped along to the next stop. "OK," Johnny said to his passenger. "I need to deliver a drawing to Mr. Rock-n-Roll."

"Mose?"

"Yeah. He's an architect, or draftsman, and he does a whale of a job—got Auto CAD machines that he prints 'em out on the computers. I taught him how to draw."

"You taught him how to draw prints?"

"Well… I taught him how to draw root cellars," he admitted, "I went to him one day and I said to him, I said, 'You can't draw the print this way.' I said, 'You can't have a root cellar with walls that are insulated that good.' I said, 'the root cellar won't work!' He looks at me and goes, 'Huh. I guess that's why mine doesn't work.' I said, 'Don't tell me you put your root cellar with pre-fab walls around it!' 'Yeah.' I said, 'Oh, gosh, don't tell me you're Amish stupid!' " Johnny laughed and laughed as they drove farther down the twisty, obstacle laden roads.

"He's in a wheelchair and he actually works with two other guys in wheelchairs. They all taught themselves to do blueprints and they're very successful."

"Wait. Mose is in a wheelchair?"

"Yeah. And he works with the one guy who lives across the road and he's quadriplegic. He can move just his mouth. He talks and it comes out on the CAD just from the talk. They are all big Phillies fans, so I'll go in there and talk to 'em about the Phillies. I go in there after they've lost four in a row and I go, 'Guys, I'm going up there. I've had it out of 'em! I think *I* can do better!' "

They pulled up to an office on the road with one vehicle in the paved spot in front of a building big enough for a dozen more automobiles. The construction portion of the building Mose's dad and brother operated was on the other side.

"Oh, the other guys aren't here," Johnny said, putting his truck into park. "Oh well, you'll get to meet Mose."

"Wait. Where are the horse and buggies? How do they get here?"

"They have cars."

72

"What? They are paralyzed and Amish. That makes no sense."

"They have drivers," he explained as they walked in the door of the small, tidy office with Mose in the center, sitting behind his desk clicking away on his computer, a blueprint machine beside him. His blonde hair, cut in the standard bowl shape, made him appear especially youthful without a beard. The office looked like any other except there was a small, low, pedestal sink outside of the bathroom that looked out of place.

Johnny handed him the drawing and explained why he needed it before telling the news.

"Oh, John," the wheel-chaired man said, stunned. "I'm sorry to hear that." He looked like he wanted to ask more questions but didn't know what to say, perhaps waiting for the punchline. "I'll be praying."

That was all the time Johnny had to spend there, in a hurry to make the rounds and tell as many people as possible before he collapsed from exhaustion. Back in the truck, they sped toward the center of town.

"So they can have CAD machines that run on electricity? Is that OK? Is it allowed because they are disabled?" Audra asked.

"No, it's because his brother never became Amish, and because he's a partner in the business, he can use electric in their business. They would have gotten special dispensation from the church to have the electric anyway. You can get special dispensation for certain things. I told you, they're not cut and dried." He turned onto the road.

"I can get special dispensation for power for sewage systems. That's not a problem. I went in one time—I didn't know I could do it —I went in one time to Antique, and I said, 'Antique,' I said, 'I need power for better sewage systems so we have healthier climates in our houses.' And he said, 'John, you need power? You just tell me and I'll go to the bishop's council and I'll get whatever power you need. You just let me know.' "

"They'll do that?"

"Yeah, yeah. And I know most of the head bishops, of course, and if one goes, 'Listen, we need to help John. John needs this, John needs that,' and they'll say, 'OK let's have a vote,' and they'll say, 'OK, John gets it. Outta here. Done.' "

"Wow!" Audra said, impressed.

"Speaking of Antique, I gotta go by and give him the update, but we'll do that on the way out. Let's go by Dan's and tell him what's going on, then we'll stop by the bank and deposit the check, then we'll go by to see Antique."

They drove back through the windy roads on the sweltering day in May that felt more like July. The fields were only barely green with corn and tobacco seedlings. As he pulled up to Hometown Builders, he yelled over to a short, young, bearded man who hardly looked old enough to be married, standing in the open garage working on a piece of machinery. "Marvin! What's up, man! Is Dan in?" He said he was, so Johnny strode into the office like he owned the place, and introduced Dan and his daughter.

The tall, bearded man rose from his chair, said hello, and reached over the table to shake Audra's hand. "You have a crazy man for a father, you know that?"

Johnny laughed. Audra agreed and took a seat in a nearby chair when Dan insisted. Dan returned to his computer's office chair and leaned back, propping his feet up on the table in the middle of the room. Marvin entered and sat on a ledge in front of the fake fire place near the door. Johnny stood at the center of attention.

"So turns out it's not lung cancer like we thought," Johnny announced. "It's prostate cancer."

"Oh, is that right?" Dan said, surprised to hear it. "Do you know the stage?"

"You have cancer?" Marvin asked, his eyes wide.

"I didn't tell you?" Dan said, before Johnny could answer. "I thought I told everybody!"

"Yeah, yeah." Johnny turned to nodded in Marvin's direction, looking hopeful. "It's prostate cancer—stage four—but that's a lot better than lung, let me tell ya."

"I want to help you, John," Dan said. "What do you need me to do? Do you need me to do any inspections for ya? I can do it all—

everything 'cept for the electrical!"

"No, no, no, no! I don't need help!" Johnny said, nearly shaking his head loose as if that was a terrible idea. *He* was the helper.

"Maybe Marvin here can do the electrical inspections," Dan suggested in jest, nodding to the young man, sparking a round of laughter.

"I've always said I'm quittin' the day the electrical inspector is Amish!" Johnny boomed to more laughs.

Dan turned to Audra. "Your dad comes in here the other day —wait, I'll do it." He sprang up from his chair and nearly ran out the door. He stomped through, mimicking his friend's stride, stopping at the half wall. As he turned with exaggerated movements toward the office area, he slapped a hand and an elbow down on top and said nonchalantly with a shrug, "Yeah, I have lung cancer. No big deal," and stomped away again, igniting uproarious laughter.

"Hey, John, you need a vacation," Dan decided, crossing back toward his computer. "How about you go with me to Indiana next weekend and relax for a little while."

"No, man, I've got a doctor's appointment on Friday, and it's going to be, like, all day long, and then another thing I've got to get on Sunday or Monday. This is going to be a full-time job," he said, shaking his head. "I might have to get Marvin here to do the electrical inspections after all!"

After a few more minutes they left. Opening the passenger side door to the small pickup, Audra wondered about the baby faced guy with the wispy beard and asked her father if he knew his age since he didn't look to be out of his teens.

"Marvin?" Johnny asked with a chuckle. "I don't know, but he has, like, eight kids!"

As before, every building site they visited with a person present, Johnny would chat for a few minutes then announce awkwardly and solemnly that he had cancer, whether he knew them well or not. Perhaps hearing himself say it over and over and getting the reactions from virtual strangers, the reality would sink in.

He didn't tell Wanda, the bank teller who said, from behind

75

the big glass window at the drive through when they deposited the check, that she'd never seen someone who could communicate with the Amish like he could. He didn't want to hear sniffles through the speaker. He dreaded telling Grace even though the new diagnosis was better. He knew she would cry again. She wasn't in the office that afternoon anyway so he had another day to deliver her the news.

Finally, they came to the last stop of the abbreviated workday and parked next to Antique's store. The man in the straw hat with the happy eyes bounced down the steps and hopped over to the driver side window to hear the news. "Well, I just wanted to give you the update," Johnny said. "I just got back from the oncologist, and it's not lung cancer like we thought. It's prostate cancer."

"Oh!" Antique said in his Dutch lilt, his eyes soft with sympathy. "And that's less aggressive, isn't it?"

"Oh, yeah! *Much* less aggressive. I've got one golfin' buddy who's had it for, like, fifteen years, and he's still goin' strong. Now, of course, my doctor said, he said, 'Listen, there's no cure. But we can work on it.' So that's what we're gonna to do. We're gonna work on it."

"Oh, well, that's good. As long as it hasn't gotten into the bones."

But cancer *was* in his bones; Johnny chose to ignore that comment.

"I hope the Good Lord's not done with me because I've got a lotta things I still wanna do. I've got four grandsons, Antique. One of 'em's gonna be just fine—that's Audra's," Johnny said, looking toward his daughter beside him. "But the other three?" He sighed and shook his head. "They need their granddad. And you Amish? Ha! You guys need me even more than they do!"

Antique chuckled. "Well, you've got a lotta people prayin' for ya."

Johnny smiled as his heart swelled at the sentiment. "Well, I better get outta here. I'll see ya, man!" He pulled out onto the road before an approaching buggy.

"You know, Dad, cancer really has a way of setting your priorities straight," Audra said, trying to strike up a deep conversation with her father. "You have to live every day like it's going to be your last. That's what I've been living with for the last eight years, and... I feel like it's been a blessing."

Johnny sighed. "Yeah, well, it is what it is." He was not yet ready to have that conversation.

***

The two days between the oncologist appointment and the appointment to set up the treatment schedule was a blur. Thoughts about the future hijacked Johnny's brain and he could think of nothing else. Who would take care of things if he wasn't there to do it? Who would make sure Patti was comfortable and take her out to dinner? Who would walk to the barn in a snowstorm to feed her horses? Who would finish the playset? Who would take the grandkids out for ice cream cones? Who would give his grandson, Wyatt, the extra attention he craved? Who would plant a garden? Who would weed the flowers? Who would mend the fences? Who would mow? Who would help the Amish now as township officials were getting more suspicious and restrictive as they saw them grow more prosperous?

When he told Grace the news, she cried exactly like he knew she would. "Grace, you look like you need a hug!" He embraced his teary co-worker and tried to assure her that even though it was stage four, it was prostate cancer. He reminded her, too, that there were many other people much worse off than him, like Mrs. Fisher, Antique's church member with lung cancer. She still didn't believe it, though she really wanted to.

As he drove around Amishland dodging buggies, the doctor's office called him with news that the full pathology was in. It was indeed prostate cancer and his PSA had been calculated. Johnny didn't know that PSA stands for Prostate Specific Antigen and healthy men have a count under 4. Nor did he know that some men elect to have their prostate removed at 4. His was over 22,000.

On his way home, he paid Huston a visit to update him with the new information. When Johnny reported his PSA and Dave's eyes "rolled back in his head," he assumed it must be bad. Real bad. For the first time, he got scared.

77

CHAPTER 10

Late May

Early Friday morning, Johnny and Patti squeezed into her little, orange car to travel to the next important appointment. He sighed heavily. "I just don't know why we have to wait to start on the chemo. I feel like it's just givin' the Bad Guys that much more time to take over more of the Good Guys," he said to his wife as if he'd been waiting a couple of months already. "I'm gonna ask the doctor about that and see if we can't start sooner."

For nearly the entire hour-long drive, Patti kept her eyes on the road while Johnny sat in the passenger seat making business calls. Each time he'd hang up, he'd tell his wife about the caller and have a story.

"That was one of my bishops up in Buck," Johnny chuckled, referencing a neighboring county. "He's got a son who's an electrician!"

"Is he Amish?"

"Yeah, he's Amish! I tell 'em all the time: 'I'm quittin' when the electrical inspector is Amish!' " Johnny cackled and threw his head back. "I took him up a book to learn more about electric—and he does his own electric—and you don't have to have a certification, so if he puts it in right, it's OK. We can sign off on it."

"I thought they weren't supposed to have anything to do with electricity."

"None are *supposed* to use it in their homes, but a lot of them do anyway and hide it from their bishop. Like, this one time I was doin' an inspection for an Amish builder and I said to him, I said, 'This is real nice, but where's the electric?' you know, just teasin' him. He looked over both shoulders to make sure nobody was listening, and said, 'John,' in a kinda hushed voice, 'I haven't brought it in yet, but I'm bringin' it in off of that telephone pole right out back. I put a false chase up in the bedroom, so I can run all my computers.'"

"What's a false chase?"

"It's something built to hide or cover up somethin' like wires or pipes. A lotta times if they're building a new house they'll put wiring behind the drywall, and, of course, they always say it's in case they want to sell it later to an English, but you can't tell me they're not installing outlets in the closets. I even had one guy tell me that's what he was gonna do because the bishops never look there!" Johnny said and cackled.

"Anyway, my bishop up in Buck," he continued, chuckling some more with a sigh and a smile, "I tell ya, him and his whole family—they are, like, wackos! I mean, they are as fun as all get-out. That bishop's brother has a saddle business, and he never introduces himself when he calls. He says, 'Top of the mornin' to ya, John!' like he's Irish. I'm like, 'Eli, you know you're Amish, right?' They're all just havin' a good time, happy to be alive," he laughed.

"Oh, and they tell me everything, honest to goodness, even things I don't want to know. This one time I was drivin' through Bart and this one Amish guy waves me down so I stop, and he's tellin' me, he says, 'John, my boy just got out of jail, so we're all real happy.'"

"Why was he in jail?"

"He was caught with his sister... if you know what I mean."

Patti kept her wide eyes on the road; her husband took another phone call.

"Now that was this guy whose whole family just left the church. Right now a lot of the ones who have been Amish are leavin' the Amish church. I knew something was up when they wanted a permit for a swimming pool. So they now drive cars, wear normal clothes. They called me up a while ago because they wanted to put a trailer at their house for the wife's mother to live in. Now, her mother's still Amish. But she's putting a trailer in with electric and she will live with them who are no longer Amish. And I said, 'How's this going to go over?' and the wife said, 'Well, we're hoping she'll come and accept it because she needs help and we want to take care of her,' this and that, so I did my very best to make sure everything was OK. And we got the trailer in and Mom moved in and she's… she's just fine."

"I bet she was thinking, 'Finally!' " Patti said with a smirk.

"Yeah. And now I'm kinda thinkin' she's now gonna live the rest of her life and have conveniences that she never dreamed she'd have." He paused for a beat and looked out the window as they whizzed past anonymous trees lining the highway. "And you know, of course, when you leave the Amish church, all the rest of the Amish are supposed to shun you. Well, here's the surprising thing: this family that left the church? Their bishop was my buddy, Antique, and his wife's job is to give the Amish kids extra education after 8th grade if they want it—'cause you know, they only go up to 8th grade. Now, this is the key: when that family left the church, they knew their kids were gonna go to English school and they were gonna be way behind, so Antique's wife took those kids-"

"*After* they left the church. She wasn't shunning them?" Patti asked like she couldn't quite believe it.

"Well, listen. After they left the church, she gave them extra schooling to help in their education in going to English school. I just heard about that. I need to tell Antique how nice I think that was."

"I think we're going to be late," Patti said, her brows touching.

"We're right on it," Johnny assured her, not wanting to stop his stream of stories or he'd have to think about his illness. "So anyway, back about three years ago when this family was still Amish, they called me up and they wanted me to help 'em and inspect their new house that was gonna be built in another township. I went to him and I said, 'if you build over here in this other township do you understand that your taxes are gonna be, like, four times higher?' And he said, 'Oh, really?' And I'm explainin' everything and his wife comes out to me and says, 'John, I don't care what it costs. I want what I want.' And I knew right then to keep my mouth shut. So they built this palatial place in this other township, I mean, just unbelievably nice. And when we're over there doin' it, uh… you notice it when you're doing an Amish house and they put electric in. Those things kinda stick out.

"Now they're lookin' to buy another business site—that's why they called, they wanted my opinion—and just to tell ya, he said to me, 'I wouldn't mind payin' two million for that business place, but I think I'm probably gonna have to pay three.' It doesn't faze them whatsoever. Unbelievable. And the funny part is, of course, he now drives a truck, and he wears all English clothes-"

"Does he have a proper haircut?"

"Oh, yeah," Johnny said, nodding his head. "That's what I was gettin' to. If you took a picture of… Oh gosh. Who's the actor that I like so much that always does the baseball movies? Uh…"

"Kevin Costner?"

"Yeah. If you took a picture of Kevin Costner when he was about 40 – 45 years old? They are carbon copies of each other. I mean, it's just staggering. I'm sittin' there lookin' at him goin', 'Oh, man!' " Johnny laughed and smiled, "If he only knew. He could be a double for Kevin Costner!"

"I think we should call them and tell them we're going to be late," she said, the permanent furrow in her brow deepening as she slowed for a red light.

He sighed and looked at his wife in exasperation. "We're not going to be late, Patti."

***

They pulled into the medical lot and took the elevator up to the second floor without saying a word to each other. The couple entered the small, green carpeted waiting room with the usual magazines littering the end tables: Men's Health, Newsweek, Better Homes and Gardens.

He checked in with a happy face for the receptionist behind the glass partition. Patti stood behind him with worry all over hers. Johnny carried yet another clipboard to their seats with more forms to fill out that looked exactly like all the other ones he'd had to fill out since this all began over a month ago. Passing the task to his wife sitting beside him, he crossed his arms over his belly, sighed nervously, and waited. He always hated waiting, but especially now. Every extra second meant gains for the Bad Guys and that was not good.

Shortly, the door to the medical rooms opened and a tall slender woman in scrubs presented herself.

"Coldiron?" she said, scanning the mostly empty room.

"Over here!" Johnny said, raising his hand and getting up from the chair. Patti followed. The nurse took the clipboard and led them to another small room where she took his blood pressure, temperature, and weighed him. On the surface he was all smiles but on the inside a war was about to be waged and tensions were high.

After an eternity that lasted only a few minutes, the door opened and in walked Dr. Caruso. They greeted each other politely and shook hands. The young doctor sat on his stool in front of his opened laptop, folded his hands, and asked his patient how he was feeling.

"I'm feeling great!" Johnny answered in an oddly excited way, nearly bouncing off his seat, adjusting his visor.

Dr. Caruso said nothing, waiting to see if he would expound on his initial answer.

"Yeah, I feel fine… and uh… I'm wondering," he said awkwardly, "I'm wondering if we can't get started on the chemo right now. I feel like the longer we wait, that's just more time for the Bad Guys to take over even more."

The doctor looked at his patient with detached compassion. "Well," he said thoughtfully, "if you are ready, I don't see any reason why we can't start your first treatment today. Is that what you want?"

"Yeah, Doc. I mean, I want my team to win. We need to give

the Good Guys some help. Hey—and while you're at it, can you do somethin' for the Phillies? I think they need more help than I do!"

Being a Phillies fan, too, the doctor chuckled to himself. "I don't think I can do anything for the Phillies, but I'll see what I can do to make that happen for you today," he said and proceeded through the rest of the examination.

Dr. Caruso announced his PSA count, which he explained stood for prostate specific antigen, a protein found in the blood when cancer is present. He didn't mention then that he'd never heard of a count so high and at first thought it was a mistake.

"The number isn't important," the doctor insisted. "What matters is if it is going up or down and how you are feeling. After three weeks we'll take that count again, and that will give an indication—but not the only indication—of how well the treatment is working."

Before leaving the room the doctor asked if he'd made his dental appointment yet, to which Johnny sheepishly admitted he hadn't. The doctor again reminded him of the importance of doing so, and he promised he'd get up with his golfing buddy who was a "real fancy dentist." More blood was drawn, and after a nurse administered the testosterone-lowering shot of Lupron, the couple anxiously waited for the next round of tests in another small room that looked like the last.

A different nurse entered. "Mr. Coldiron?"

"That's me!" Johnny exclaimed in his big voice with a smile to match.

"Well, you're in a good mood!" the nurse said with her own big, friendly smile. "I'm Lisa. Dr. Caruso has arranged for you to start your treatment today."

"Oh, wow!" Patti said as if *her* life depended on it.

"Wonderful! Wonderful!" Johnny nearly shouted, and clapped his hands. "Where is that guy? I want to shake his hand!"

After a bone scan, Lisa led the couple into the big, open room with the olive-green, over-stuffed vinyl chemo dispensing chairs identical to the room in Exton where they had explained how the procedure works. "You're gonna have your work cut out for you with my arms," he said and displayed his vein-free arms as he settled into his chair. Patti watched nervously as the nurse wheeled the chemo dispensing machine that looked like a modern parking meter toward her husband then positioned it between the two chairs.

After searching for longer than usual for a suitable place on the patient's arm to stick a needle, she exclaimed, "You weren't kidding when you said your veins were hard to find!" The nurse laughed and finally managed to locate one on his hand. "OK. Now, this might feel weird at first, but you'll get used to it."

The battle began as the first dose of chemo began coursing through his body.

"Are you OK?" Lisa asked.

"Oh, yeah!" Johnny swore. "I'm excited to get this show on the road!"

"I've never had someone so excited to get chemo before!" the nurse said with a grin. "You'll be hooked up to this for an hour. If at any point you start to feel discomfort let me know immediately."

"We will," Patti answered anxiously knowing her husband would never admit to discomfort himself. She was pretty sure that's how the cancer was allowed to spread as far as it did in the first place.

Lisa walked over to her station and gazed at her computer screen. Suddenly her eyes widened in alarm when she noticed his PSA. "Now, don't you worry," she said rushing back over to Johnny to check the connection that she had just checked. "Everything's going to be all right. You are in good hands here."

Johnny laughed. "Oh, I'm not worried. I've got a lotta people prayin' for me!"

"Well, that's good. I'm going to pray for you, too," she promised and went about bustling back and forth.

It wasn't long before he had his phone to his ear again, listening to messages and returning calls. Patti snapped a picture of him while hooked up to the chemo machine and posted it on Facebook along with the caption, "Chemo can't slow him down. Work to do ahead!"

***

Immediately people replied. This being the first official announcement that Johnny had been diagnosed with cancer, Audra shared the post. So did Dolly. Brooke did, too. Word spread and soon people he hadn't talked to for years were calling or texting with their words of encouragement and pledging prayers. The chemo didn't seem to affect him at all. He didn't even feel nauseous afterward, which he thanked God for.

"I tell ya, everywhere I go people come up to me and say things like 'Oh, I heard the news' and 'We're prayin' for you, John,'" he said to Audra when she called on Friday to check up on him and to remind him it was his anniversary. "I'm like, 'Am I dying?'" He chuckled softly. "It's just overwhelming. Then, of course, because of this medicine I'm on, whenever anyone is nice to me I get emotional. It's embarrassing!" he cried, emphasizing his level of discomfort. "Like, I was over at the Hometown Kitchen in Georgetown for lunch since the doctor said I need to eat regular meals, and I go to pay and the girl there says 'It's already been paid for,' and I start tearin' up. Grace says her zoning officer is goin' through menopause." He laughed at her joke in an awkward kind of way then sighed.

"Oh, on Sunday," he continued, "I went over to get this shot I have to get after chemo to boost my white blood cell count, and I was in the parking lot goin' in and this nurse who helped me on Friday—she's real cool, her name is Lisa—and she saw me from across the parking lot. Now, I'm sure she's sees hundreds of people, and she only met me once and she yells, 'John. John!' and I look over and it's her. And she comes over and gives me a big hug and asks me how I am and tells me again that everything's gonna be alright. It's just been real neat.

"She wasn't there today, though. Dolly went with me this time because your mom had to work and we were in the room talkin' about this and that, and the doctor asked me again if I'd gone to the dentist. When I said I hadn't done that yet, he looked at Dolly and said, 'Now I'm making you responsible to see that your dad gets to

85

the dentist!' So, I've got to get Dolly off the hook and go see my buddy, Nemo. He's a dentist. A real good one, too.

"Oh, and there was this one Amish guy who I haven't seen in probably ten years who put the roof on our big barn—do you remember that? Well, he called and left a message because he heard. I saved it on my phone."

Audra chuckled and asked if that was the reason his phone had been unable to take more messages for days—he was saving all of them. He denied it, insisting that was the only message he had saved and it was full because people had just been calling so much.

"He said that his wife hadn't stopped cryin' since she heard because she had always said that if he died I was her backup!" Johnny laughed and laughed. "Now, see, that's real unusual for a man to say."

He sighed and lamented that he had wanted to come visit her sometime that summer but now felt tied down with his treatment schedule. "It's like every day I've got to get a shot or have blood drawn," he complained, narrowly missing a boy on a wagon as he came over the hill. "It's like a full-time job!"

"Don't worry about it, Dad. I'm coming to see you again on your next chemo appointment."

"Oh, you are? That's wonderful!" He always looked forward to her visits. Maybe she would ride around Amishland with him again and she could tape more stories.

"Are you and mom doing anything for your anniversary?"

"Well, we're going out tomorrow night with friends. We'll probably go out to eat somewhere tonight, too. It just kind of snuck up on us with everything going on."

"Oh, by the way, Mamaw is super upset about this and can't sleep. She thinks you are going to Hell because you don't go to church anymore."

"Oh, geez," he sighed. "I'll have to go over there."

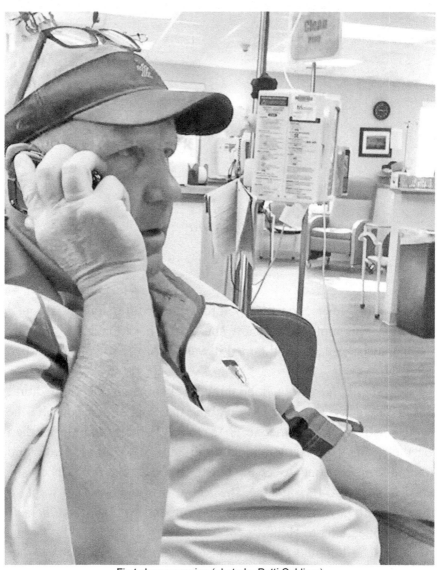

First chemo session (photo by Patti Coldiron)

CHAPTER 11

End of May

After another inspection and before going home, Johnny stopped over to see his mother. He knew she was going to take the news of his diagnosis hard, but had hoped it wasn't for the reason Audra had said.

I should have known, he thought. If someone she knew didn't go to church anymore, she fretted about that soul's future despite the Baptist belief that if someone is "saved"—believes that Jesus died for their sins—they automatically go to heaven after death and nothing can be done to change that. It made no difference; she worried anyway. If someone she knew died who never went to church at all, at his funeral she would sob and wail as if she herself were the one going to Hell.

As he hobbled slowly and stiffly up the three steps to her deck, the diminutive matriarch stood at the open doorway with a pained expression, having already spotted her oldest child pulling up.

"Hello, Mom," he said, kissing her on the forehead and limping past her to the kitchen. "How are you?"

"Oh, Johnny," she said in her high-pitched, southern twang, "I'm terrible! I cain't sleep at all, I been so worried about you." She watched him in anguish, wringing her arthritic hands as he staggered to the kitchen table to sit.

"Do you want anything to eat?" the 84-year-old woman asked, looking like she was about to burst into tears.

"No thanks, Mom. I'm stuffed."

"Oh, I'm just so worried!" she said, barely holding back the tidal wave, and began heating up some leftover beans and cornbread anyway. "I'm tellin' ya, Johnny. You need to get back in church!"

Johnny said nothing. When his mother got out the strawberry pie from the refrigerator, she couldn't hold back the floodgates any longer. "I don't want you to go to Hell!" she wailed with conviction and burst into heaving, bitter tears.

Johnny pleaded with her to stop crying. "Mom. I'm not going to Hell. Stop thinkin' that!"

She sobbed even louder. "I cain't, Johnny! The Bible says you should convene with others!" she insisted convinced his eternal life depended on it.

"Mom," he said and smiled. "You don't understand. I convene all day long with the Amish. Trust me. You have no idea what it's like up there and how many people I got prayin' for me. It's like I'm in one big prayer service when I'm there."

Her face brightened and the sobbing lessened somewhat.

"I'll take you around with me one day so you can see for yourself. I'm not going to Hell."

He stood and gave her a big hug, squeezing tears out of her again. "Now, stop your worryin'!" She sniffled and looked up at him with a sad but hopeful smile. After stuffing down a plate of food to appease his mother, he said goodbye and drove home, hoping what he had said was the truth.

***

Saturday night, finally spending his gift certificate Grace had given him, he took Patti to The Bullfrog Inn to meet his two best friends and their wives. Walking in, he spotted the owner and told him all about the dry wells that The Hometown Kitchen, their competitor uphill, were going to install that would improve their standing water problems. Meanwhile Patti walked on to their table where the

Hustons and the Parrishes sat looking at menus.

Finally, Mr. Coldiron crossed the checkered floor of the long, dimly lit, wood-paneled sports bar to join his friends. Cheryl, the baby of the group with kind eyes and long, dark hair full of body, asked Johnny about the doctor appointments and how he was feeling. He told them all about how he talked the doctor into starting early and the nurse, Lisa, who remembered him, and how everyone's been so nice but with the Lupron it makes him tear up. Aileen, Frank's wife, asked how his four kids were reacting. He told her Dolly went to his last appointment with him and that Audra calls all the time but though he lives in the same house with his son, Young John, they never talk much except when they have to about work.

"What is really surprising is Brooke," he said about his estranged middle daughter.

"Yeah, she's taking it the hardest," Patti added between bites of ribs.

"Yeah, well, you know, she would barely say two words to me before, and last Saturday I go and knock on her door to pick up her son Wyatt for his golf lesson—I take him and Zander every Saturday up to Del Castle—and she said, she goes, 'I want to go, too!' I was like, 'What?' So she came and we had a real nice time. We talked the whole time, and she asked me questions and made an effort to be nice—you know, that's real hard for her—then afterward when I was at home she sent me a text that said, 'Even though you've done some stupid stuff, I still love you.' And that was nice—of course she had to qualify it," he said, allowing a hint of disdain to show through. "But that's OK. I still appreciated it. And afterward she invited me and Patti over to hang out at her pool in the backyard."

"Oh, she got a pool installed?" asked Aileen Parrish, a tall, thin woman with sharp, pale features that looked striking against her short dark hair.

"I didn't tell you that?" Patti said to her long-time friend. They had met in the 80's, both couples interested in Arabian horses, but the friendship was cemented when Frank and Johnny began playing golf together.

"I don't think so. And this is in back of your old house, right?"

Patti nodded and sighed. She reached for another rib.

"Oh, yeah," Johnny said, taking over, "she's made it real nice. There's a shallow shelf covered with, like, ankle deep water that's big enough for a couple chairs and shaded by a big umbrella. She even went out and bought the chairs and umbrella just for us!" He took a drink of his ice water and put it down with a sigh like it was the best thing ever. "It's real nice, especially since it's been so hot already."

Everyone agreed that it had been unusually hot for late May with every day of the past week in the mid 80's. Johnny took a bite of a rib and started a story with his mouth full.

"So I had this one Amishman in Strasburg call me up yesterday, and he said, 'John. I love my insulation.' Now, it'd been a year since I talked to him. His family sold their farm for several million dollars and built them new houses, the two brothers did. This one brother built a house so cotton-pickin' efficient as far as heat and thermal was concerned, I argued with him that he was making the house too tight. He said, 'Does it meet code?' and I said, 'Yeah, it meets code.' He says, 'Well, I'm gonna do it,' and he sprayed foam six inches thick the entire envelope of the house.

"So he calls me up and I said, 'Well, I'm certainly glad you love your insulation because you paid for it, and I'm happy to hear that you're happy. That's wonderful.' And he goes, 'Well, do you want to know why I'm so happy?' I says, 'Yeah. Go ahead, tell me.' He says, 'Well, back in the old days in the old farmhouse when we had a week of hot weather like this,' he said, 'me and the boys would have to sleep outside under the trees.' He said, 'We're sleeping upstairs.' He said, 'That insulation also keeps out the heat.' And I went, 'Whoa! I hadn't thought about that—keepin' *out* the heat.' I said, 'That's wonderful!' He says, 'It does so good,' he said, 'all the radiant pipes I put in for heat, I'm gonna start runnin' cold water through them and it will be like air conditioning,' " Johnny laughed, "Why not?"

"And does that work?" Frank asked.

91

"Yes! It works!" he swore, though he just assumed. "Oh, they are very, very ingenious."

Just then, the hostess walked passed them, menus in her arms, leading the latest diners to their seats.

"John!" Grace said, nearly bumping into him on the way.

"Hey hey!" Johnny said and struggled to stand up. "Chester, my man!"

They shook hands, and Johnny introduced everyone to Chester, his head supervisor, and his wife, Grace, the township's secretary and the his "work wife" (as Patti referred to her). Grace said she felt like she knew Frank and Huston since she'd heard all the golfing stories and cited the U-Haul story as her favorite. Huston laughed, having lived it. Grace asked if Johnny was using the gift certificate she and Chester gave him. He said he was.

"Now, I don't want you to worry about that hearing," Grace insisted in her motherly way. "You have bigger fish to fry!"

He insisted he wasn't worried, but that wasn't exactly true.

When the couple left for their table, Patti turned to Johnny with her brow extra furrowed. "Chester doesn't look so good," she whispered. "I think there's something wrong with him."

Johnny brushed it off as nothing. Aileen asked about the hearing that Grace referenced. He rubbed his face, and filled them in on the Nickle Mines situation: how he had accidentally walked in on his three supervisors in the township building discussing road costs, how Bill said he wanted the old building across from his house torn down, and how Bill told Johnny he could do whatever he wanted with that project if he could make that happen.

"Well, you know," began Aileen, a supervisor in her own township, "supervisors can't make decisions unless the public can witness it, like at a hearing."

Johnny, his wheels turning, tucked that piece of information away to be used at a later date as everyone finished their meals. When the plates were taken away, the women chatted amongst themselves while the men talked about their favorite subject.

"J.D.," Huston said, "I'm golfing in a tournament tomorrow and we need one more person. Ronnie doesn't know if he can come now. It's me, Tommy Ho, and Nemo since Frankie here's being a baby on the bench with a hurt shoulder." Frank, who had injured his shoulder on their ill-fated golfing trip and had reconstructive surgery scheduled, chuckled self consciously.

"I thought I could persuade you to come out and redeem yourself."

Huston could always talk Johnny into golfing, and they both knew it. "Well, you know what?" Johnny said after thinking about it for a couple seconds. "I still can't walk real good and I'm gonna be just terrible probably, but if Nemo's gonna be there I can talk to him about doin' my dental work."

***

Still unable to walk very easily but determined to play a round with his buddies, the inspector pulled his truck as close to the clubhouse as he could get. Rolling his golf bag behind him, he limped into the clubhouse where Huston and Tommy, having already checked in, waited for the rest of their group to show up.

"How are you feelin', J.D.?" asked Davy Huston. The question sounded eerily familiar. Johnny remembered constantly asking that very same question when his friend was first diagnosed with stage four colon cancer. Now it was his turn, and he looked to Davy as inspiration.

"I'm feelin' great!" he said with a smile, though he always said that. He could be bleeding out of his ears and still answer the same way. Since the chemo he felt different somehow but couldn't put his finger on it. "Don't go easy on me, though."

"Don't worry," Huston assured him, "I still plan on taking your money."

The guys played their own version of the golf game, "Wolf," that was so unusual that Sports Illustrated did an article on it once.

"Man, I tell ya," Johnny started and shook his head, looking toward the ground. "The doctor gave me this shot that lowers my testosterone, and it's, like, turning me into a woman!"

"You're the ugliest woman I've ever seen," Huston teased.

93

"Oh, no. You haven't seen ugly until you've seen some of the old Amish women!" Johnny laughed shaking his head. "I shouldn't say that. They're just very plain, but that's what they want to be. None of the women wear makeup, and they pull their hair back so tight into those buns that a lot of the older ones are goin' a little bald up there at their part."

"Hey, you fit right in!" Tommy Ho teased.

Johnny chuckled. "They are sweethearts though, and so much fun," he said, gearing up for a story. "This one time I was doing this inspection on this house for this Amish family I know real well. And I go to Mom—that's what they call her, she's 91—and I went in her room where she was—and Mom's real spry—she's just up and goin' all the time, and I said, 'Mom, you're awful spry. Any chance you're lookin' for a man?' "

The men laughed at the inappropriate comment.

"She goes, 'John! No!' I said, 'Well, I don't know. Boy, you're a real go-getter,' I said, 'And you're so good lookin'!' So the next time I'm there her daughter, who's seventy-something, comes to me and she goes, 'John, you're not going to believe how you picked Mom's spirits up,' she goes, 'She stands at the windows staring, waiting for you to come back!' "

"Aw, man, you got Great Grandma's hopes up!" Tommy Ho said.

Johnny chuckled and continued. "Well, one day this winter I'm over there getting the old man to sign somethin' on the new house and him and his buddies—now, these are guys all in their late seventies—they're out in the barn pitchin' quoits."

"A quoit? What's that?" asked Huston, always ready to learn a new game.

"A quoit is a round rubber circle and it's closed all the way around. You play it like horseshoes, but it's harder because it's a circle. It's a very, very European game. Anyway, here's these old guys in there, throwin' quoits in the wintertime in the barn, and Mom, ninety-one, she's in there keeping score. Of course, I go in there, I go, 'I should have known, Mom, you'd be in here with all the men!' " Johnny laughed again.

"So when we moved them in, Mom had her own little bedroom and they had put her bed in and it was a twin. And I looked at her and I said, shakin' my head, I said, 'Oh, Mom, that ain't gonna work,'" he laughed, "And she goes, 'Oh, John!'"

"How old's this lady again?" Tommy asked.

"She's 91. So, I saw the other sister one day and I said, 'Did you hear what I told Mom?' She goes, 'Oh yeah,' she goes, 'Mom loves you!'"

Nemo walked through the door a few minutes late to join the men who were chuckling over Johnny's anecdotes. They greeted the dentist and headed out toward the practice green with their clubs.

"What's so funny?"

"J.D. was just tellin' us about Amish women. He says they're uglier than he is," Huston paraphrased as he put a ball down and lined it up with the hole.

"Well... I... that's not exactly what I said," Johnny insisted, backtracking. "Now, all the Amish have awful teeth. I don't know what kind of dentist they go to, Nemo, but I don't think their dentist went to the same school as you!"

"Oh yeah?" Nemo grinned. "Let's not get off track here. So there aren't any good looking Amish women?"

"Oh, no, there are a few," Johnny chuckled. "In fact, I kep' hearin' about this one woman whose husband turned Amish for her."

"Holy shit. How does that happen?" Nemo said with a grin, gripping his new putter. "Was the guy driving through Lancaster thinking to himself, 'You know what? I have it too easy with all this driving and electricity. I'm going to find a nice Amish woman and milk cows. In the dark.'" He took a practice putt and missed.

"Man, she must have been smokin' hot to turn Amish for!" Huston said.

"Yeah, that's what I'm thinkin'. So I'm like, man, I gotta meet this lady. Then one day right out of the blue I get a call from this Amish guy. He says, 'John, I need your help. Can you come over here. I have a daughter who lives in Indiana, and her husband left her, and she's going to move back here, and I have to build her a house as soon as possible.' So I drive straight over, set down with

95

him, and I tell him what I can do with the permits and how fast he can have them, this and that. Then I said, 'She lives in Indiana and her husband left her? That's real unusual.' Then he said, he said, 'Well, he used to be English.' I was like, 'Oh my goodness. I found her!' " Johnny paused a moment to laugh and line up his practice putt.

"So did you get to meet her?" Tommy Ho asked.

"No, not then. She decided not to move after all. A couple years later I'm down in Peach Bottom, and I was asked to help a lady who had a greenhouse. I get there and I'm helping her, and I said to her, I said, 'You're not married?'—because she had two kids there and it's real unusual for there to be an unmarried Amish woman with kids—and she said, 'Well, yes, I am, but my husband lives in Indiana.' And I said, 'Are you so-and-so's daughter?' 'Yeah.' And I said, 'Your husband used to be English and is now again?' 'Yeah.' " The ball missed the cup by a couple inches.

"So, I'm trying to get to the bottom of this. I said, 'Does he ever come back here? Does he take care of the kids?' She said, 'Yeah, he comes back and visits and takes care of the kids.' I says, 'And he went and got a divorce?' She goes, 'Yeah.' I said, 'But you don't consider yourself divorced?' 'No.' And I said, 'OK, but you still consider yourself married?' 'Yeah.' And I'm just shakin' my head. I said, 'So... you live like this, and he can just come and go as he pleases? He doesn't sound like he's a real nice guy.'

" 'Oh no, John. He's a very nice man,' she says, 'He's just confused and he has some issues, but he's a very nice man and a wonderful father.' I'm like, 'What? This makes no sense whatsoever.'

"So I said, 'Well, let me tell you somethin'. This has been a real treat for me because you are someone I've been wanting to meet for several years now, and yes, I was right.' She goes, 'You were right? About what?' I says, 'You're pretty good lookin'!' " Johnny threw his head back cackling, while the other golfers chuckled along.

"So, does he get conjugal visits or what?" Huston asked.

"That's what my thought was. Does she sleep with him when he comes home? I couldn't ask that. That's... I can get away with a lot of things, but I don't think I could get away with that. Well, now, maybe later as I get to know her better!"

"Don't tell Patti that!" Huston warned.

"Oh, God!" Johnny said, throwing his head back to laugh, looking to the clear, blue sky. "I need to get a cart."

Huston offered to get the cart for him knowing he couldn't easily walk, and Johnny didn't protest. Tommy joined him for a second cart while Nemo remained on the putting green getting used to his new club. He asked Johnny how he was feeling and he told him all about talking the doctor into starting the chemo right away and how he could still feel the tingling.

"Yeah, it's like the Good Guys are searching out the Bad Guys and zapping them. It's a really weird feeling." He told him about the Lupron shot and that it's turning him into a woman and that's how he got to talking about the Amish women. Awkwardly, he brought up needing some dental work before he could take the bone strengthening medicine when the chemo sessions are all over, and how he has to get Dolly off the hook.

"J.D., I want to help you out. Come to my office tomorrow and I'll squeeze you in," Nemo said. Though it was exactly what Johnny had hoped, he pretended to protest, citing the dentist's busy schedule, and not wanting to be a bother. When Nemo insisted, the new patient insisted on paying.

"Hey, Nemo, if you don't want to take his money, I will," Huston yelled from behind the wheel of his golf cart. Johnny loaded his clubs in the back of Huston's ride and Nemo in Tommy's. At the first hole, the men stood in a circle and dropped a tee on the ground as they did at the start of every round.

"Looks like you're first, Tommy," Huston announced when the tip of the tee pointed in his direction. "J.D.'s next, then me, then Captain Nemo."

"So we're playin' for Nemo dollars?" J.D. asked, teasing his friend, Dr. Niemoeller who hated losing and insisted on playing for half a dollar to everyone's whole one despite his three palatial residences.

"Yeah. What else?" Nemo said with a grin.

CHAPTER 12

Early June

Monday morning Johnny arrived at Nemo's dental office and, just like his friend had promised, he squeezed him in. In the dentist chair before his buddy arrived, the hygienist struck up a conversation with the inspector.

"Dr. Niemoeller tells me you work with the Amish and you know a lot about them," she said, clipping the paper bib around his neck. She confessed her fascination with the Amish ever since the show, *The Amish Mafia*. Before she could ask, Johnny recited the same stories he told everyone when that subject came up.

He impressed her with the party he was going to that weekend that a wealthy Amish businessman was throwing, and that he, incidentally, was the one who housed classes temporarily in his garage after the infamous school was torn down. She couldn't believe there were wealthy Amishmen; she also couldn't believe that they had garages, let alone *three-car* garages.

He told her, too, about his first day as the zoning officer of Bart and how sick to death everybody had gotten of "New York" (meaning the press) by the time it was all over.

"And after the shooting, there were some things that happened during the rehabilitation of the kids that was absolutely beyond belief. Really weird stuff," he said mysteriously, lifting his eyebrows. "They say that when the shooter started opening fire, all the kids started running, and they ran until they were out of the school.

"Now. After the girls were shot and the shooter shot himself, they gathered those kids—*who were not together again until **after** they went through therapy,*" he said, emphasizing the last part, and paused, adding to the drama. "During therapy, they interviewed each kid individually and asked them all the same thing: 'Why did you run?'" He paused again and waited for her to respond.

"What did they say?"

"Well. Every single one of the kids said exactly the same thing," he said, nearly whispering, and looked into her transfixed face, lifting his eyebrows, slightly less bushy than before. "They said, 'The angel told us to run.'"

She was, as he had hoped, thoroughly mesmerized by his story, but couldn't launch into another one since his buddy, Nemo, had arrived to look in his mouth.

"Whenever I need something done at my house, Johnny always sends me an Amishman," Dr. Niemoeller told his hygienist. "They're good, but they are not cheap!"

Had Johnny not had a mouthful of dental equipment, he would have told her how the Amish sell their wares worldwide on the internet, like beehives and the scooters they ride that look like bicycles that the Flintstones might have used. That would have totally blown her mind.

While Nemo did the examination, grumbling the whole time about the other golfers always taking his money, he found two teeth that needed pulling and two that required root canals. "Tell your doctor you have remarkably strong bones," Nemo said, struggling to pull out the second one. Johnny was proud of that remark. He was strong. Maybe he didn't even need the bone-strengthening medicine after his treatment was all over. In any case, after the extractions there was no more extra time left, and he would have to return another day for the root canals.

Amishwoman on scooter (photo by Terry Tabb)

***

The next day, he stopped by his mother's house in the morning as usual, but not to eat biscuits and gravy. This time it was to ask her if she would ride with him on his inspection rounds that day so she could see for herself what kind of people he associated with all day long. "I swear, Mom," he said, "I've been caught in prayer service more than once."

She accepted his invitation; he cleared out his passenger seat for his mother and together they rode around Amishland. As he darted from inspection to inspection, everyone who would listen heard the story: first, that he had prostate cancer (if they didn't already know), then next, how he talked his doctor into starting treatment immediately. They always offered prayers; he always accepted. Ruth witnessed it all.

They stopped at Hometown Builders so he could introduce the woman who brought him into the world to Dan and his wife. As

Liz busily washed the windows, Ruth told her how much she loved housework, and especially cleaning windows and mirrors.

"But I guess you don't have no mirrors," Ruth said, having always heard the Amish weren't allowed to see their own images, whether it be in a picture or a reflection.

"Of course we have mirrors!" Liz said, grinning. "How else could I do my hair in the mornin'?"

While dodging buggies over hills and around turns through the lush countryside, Johnny pointed out places of interest to his mother like a private tourguide: the new house that stood where the old farmhouse was where the movie with Harrison Ford was filmed (though she had no idea who he was), the Nickel Mines project where the county's first self-serve grocery store had been (never mentioning his current problem with it), and the fallow field where the infamous schoolhouse once stood. He also showed her, by driving down the secluded driveway, where the new school had been built.

"See that farm over there?" he said, sticking his arm out the open window to point out a white farmhouse, clothes waving like banners in the summer breeze from a line that stretched from the house to the nearest of their two big red barns. She turned her head to look as they rolled up and down hills, corn growing up on either side. "That family had a girl who was killed in the school. They had five boys and then after five boys they finally had a little girl, and she was one of the girls killed in the school. And they were just heartbroken that they had waited so long for a girl and that's what happened. And the mother wrote stories in the Lancaster paper about how they had to forgive and she was, like, the leader of the community in wishing forgiveness and speaking forgiveness," Johnny said drifting to the other side of the road, nearly hitting a buggy head on, swerving at the last second.

"And as all this was going on?" He paused and looked over to his special passenger beside him, "The mother become pregnant and had another little girl. So, of course, when I heard I went over there to visit. We hugged. She knows it was sent special for her. So, she got what she wanted," he chuckled and sighed contentedly. "And that's the kind of things that make them and this place extra special."

Ruth admired the flowerbeds they passed, tended by the Amish ladies and children, alive with red, pink, and purple impatiens, petunias, and begonias. She marveled at the manicured lawns trimmed with rotary mowers.

Almost out of Georgetown, Johnny spotted a familiar face walking along the road. He pulled up beside him and leaned over his mother to take a picture with his phone just as the bishop realized what was happening. "Hey, man! I gotta update your Facebook page!" the inspector teased with a straight face, his truck creeping along slower than a buggy. Antique giggled in his funny, high-pitched way. "Oh, John, you're out of control!" The inspector zoomed away before a car could dodge him.

Johnny made sure his mother knew that she had just met a very high ranking and influential bishop in the Amish church, and he was the one who had invited him to be a guest preacher.

"But you just took a picture of him! I thought they cain't have no pictures."

"Oh, I just tease him all the time. He loves it. This one time I was over next to his place and we were talkin' and I said, 'Antique, the Amish are changing much faster than the English.' He said, 'Yep, you're right.' He says, 'Why do you think it is?' And I said, 'Well, I know exactly why it is. It's because you have more money. Honest to God, you Amish have more money than the English now.' And he said, 'Yep. You're right, John. Money's the root of all evil.' I went, 'Antique. Use the King James version of the Bible. It does not say that. I'll tell you exactly what it says. Go get it!' So he goes in and here he comes back out holding his Bible, and his eyes got big as saucers and I says, 'Antique, it says the *love* of money is the root of all evil. Now, you listen,' I says, 'That's what it says.' And he goes, 'Well, that's... well... but... but it meant-' I go, 'No, don't give me what you *think* it meant. Read what it says. It says the LOVE of money,' I says, 'You can have a whole lot of money, Antique, and I hope you do, and I hope you use it for good purposes and do good things with it 'cause that's what it is meant for and that's why it was given to you.' "

"That's exactly right!" Ruth agreed, nodding her head, hands folded in her lap.

"He sit there, and he says, 'OK. You're right, John. You're absolutely right.' See, and that's how come, when I said to him, 'When are you gonna invite me to be the guest preacher?' he says, 'Anytime you want, John.' " Johnny chuckled at one of his favorite stories. "Now, he was probably just joking about that, but he said it —twice!"

Randy Coldiron, Ruth Coldiron, and Johnny Coldiron, Easter 2016.
(photo by Patti Coldiron)

Amish kids cutting grass with rotary mower (photo by Terry Tabb)

***

Late Friday afternoon after a busy week of appointments and inspections, Johnny, his wife, and grandson, Zander, traveled to the party that Amos King held every year. At 5:00 pm, the sun still shone brightly in the blue, cloudless sky; the air so warm and still and the scene so perfect, it could have been a movie set. The beautifully landscaped field surrounded by trees behind the Kings' construction business featured a pond with a picturesque gazebo at its edge and a single giant oak tree from which hung a tire swing. As they arrived, men in straw hats stood in a boom raised as high as the tree and threw out candy to the children. The year before, Amos had hired a helicopter to do the job.

The usual mix of Amish and English attended, eating and chatting in and around the pavilion by a large tent that covered a buffet loaded with picnic food. Everyone who knew Johnny and his condition asked the inspector about his health; those who didn't know of his illness were informed and pledged prayers.

As Zander took turns with the other boys on the tire swing, Dan and Liz arrived. Spotting the inspector, they hurried over to say hello and to finally meet his wife. Johnny also introduced Patti to the host and his wife, Elsie, whom she especially liked because "She's not as skinny as the other Amish women."

After filling their plates with meatballs, coleslaw, and potato salad, they all sat at one of the picnic tables under the pavilion and asked Johnny for the update on his health. He told them about getting his teeth pulled and the appointment the following Monday to get his port installed that will administer the remaining five doses of chemo.

"I was at the doctor's this morning and he asked me how I was feelin', and, of course, I told him I'm feelin' great. He asked me, he goes, 'Have you felt any effects of the chemo?' And at first I was like, 'No, nothin' '—because I been feelin' great, not gotten sick because of it—then I remembered this one day I was ridin' around Bart on my way to check up on this Amish guy who was movin' too much dirt—his bishop had called to tell me—and, of course, I had my windows down and I start seein' all this stuff flyin' around the truck, and I'm like, 'What the heck is this?' I keep drivin,' and I look in my mirror and I realize it was my hair!" Johnny laughed. His audience laughed with him.

"You didn't have too much there to begin with," Dan pointed out mischievously. Johnny smiled and rubbed his slick head.

"So when's your next chemo session?" Elsie asked.

"It's next Friday, and my daughter Audra's comin' for that one. She's the one helping me with my book."

"You're writing a book?" Elsie asked, her beautiful blue eyes round.

Johnny chuckled, "Well… she's prob'ly gonna be doin' most of the writing since I'm just a dumb hillbilly," he said, causing Patti to roll her eyes, "but it's gonna be all about my experiences with the Amish. I told Antique we were doin' it, and he said he didn't want his name used so, I said, 'Ok, what can we call you?' He goes, 'You can just call me Antique!' "

Dan, Liz, Amos, and Elsie doubled over in laughter.

"Why is that so funny?" Patti asked, totally confused.

"Because that's what everybody knows him by! Most people don't even know his real name!" Johnny explained, still chuckling.

"I bet you'll have a lot of stories about Gabriel in there," Amos said, taking a bite of his potato salad.

"Are you kiddin'? The whole book could be about him!" Johnny joked.

"There was one story about him you threatened to tell us a while ago but you never did," said Liz. "Somethin' about plumbing."

"Oh. That's a good one. It's definitely gonna be in the book. I never told you that one?" he said, adjusting himself in his seat, preparing to spin the tale. "Patti, this one's about the Amish guy who owns the property up at Nickel Mines that's a pain in my backside-"

"Do you mean the project or Gabriel?" Dan asked.

"Both!" he said, causing those around him to chuckle. "So in this one project he had told his plumber to route the plumbing into a tank which was not supposed to be used. Now, the tank normally woulda had to be taken away, but I told him the tank could stay just for gray water, OK?

"Well, next time I go to check up on him, he's usin' the tank for sewage water. I start screamin' the legalities of the situation," Johnny said, beginning to reenact the scene complete with raised voice and finger pointing, " 'All black water has to go to a certain tank, and you've plumbed it to go into that illegal tank that I said you could use for gray water only,' I said, 'What you've done with that tank is never going to be allowed in my lifetime! Do you understand me?'

"He looked at me and said, 'No'." Johnny paused to look around the room. "So I said the exact same words louder and asked him again if he understood me, and again he said, 'No.'

"So then I went down to a very, very low whisper," Johnny said, whispering also in demonstration, " 'Well then, that's fine,' I said. 'What I'll do is go back to the township and get a hold of my solicitor (our township lawyer), and I'll put a red card (a stop work order) on your project,' and I said, 'And nothing will ever happen on this project until I get exactly what I want. Do you understand me now?'

"He looked at me," Johnny paused strategically to add to the drama, "and that time he said 'Yes.'

"So I looked over at the plumber and I said, 'All right. Rip out everything!' I looked at Gabriel and I said, 'Now you've got an extra inspection,' I said. 'The tank that I originally said could stay will stay, but it's now going to be filled with stone and concrete. It will never be used,' I said. 'Now, I'll throw an extra inspection on the mason to make sure I get exactly what I want.' And, of course, Mose's dad was the mason, so I left the project and headed straight over to their office to tell him what he had to do," Johnny paused. "Speaking of Mose," he shook his head, "I still can't believe you guys never told me he was Mick Jagger!"

"I thought you knew," Dan said with a shrug.

Johnny chuckled. "So anyway," he continued, "on my way there to Mose's place, the plumber calls me, and he says, 'John, I understood you the first time you said it!' And I said, 'I know you did.' I said, 'And furthermore, you love me because you got two jobs in one: the first job that you've got to rip out, and the second job that you got to do right!' " Johnny's big laugh eventually devolved into a chuckle and then a sigh.

"So Gabe listens to me now, and if I can help him I will, because as I tell him all the time, 'The more business you do, and the more you can increase commercial properties, the more taxes you pay and therefore my regular people in regular houses do not have to pay as much in taxes.' Of course, he doesn't want to hear that, but he knows I'm right, and it's a fact of life."

Amos asked if Bill was still mad about the concrete being poured, word having traveled through the grapevine. Johnny told him the whole situation and that the supervisor had requested a hearing, much to his chagrin. Amos suggested Johnny go to Bill's house and talk to him; if Bill had any common sense at all, he would see reason and the misunderstanding could be settled that way. The inspector agreed and decided to pay his supervisor a visit the next day.

As the party continued, a baseball game began with young Amish men batting and running around the bases barefoot in their long black pants held up by suspenders over rolled up long-sleeved button-down shirts. As Johnny ate and watched the game, he turned to his wife. "This is a little piece of Americana right here," he said and sighed contentedly.

She rolled her eyes. "This is *not* Americana, Johnny."

Gazebo around the pond at the party.

CHAPTER 13

June 12

The following Wednesday, Johnny left early for his second chemo session with Patti and Audra along for support. On the way, he conducted business from the backseat of the little orange car, where he insisted on sitting, looking rather comical like a clown on a miniature bicycle. His wife and daughter caught up in the front: Patti talked about the horse she sold and the plans she had for the money she'd saved so far; Audra told her about Mamaw's visit a couple weeks ago when they picked strawberries and garlic scapes (a first for Ruth), and hung laundry. They both marveled at the difference her new knee made; this time last year she had seemed to be on a downward slide, but now, incredibly, she had bounced back to her busy old self.

"Johnny, did you ever go to talk to that supervisor who's been giving you trouble?" Patti asked when she heard her husband recite his signature ending for phone calls: "Pray for me, man… Talk to ya." She didn't know the answer to her question because they rarely talked. At home they watched separate TVs in separate rooms, even when they watched the same show; she hung out on Facebook; he shunned social media. When they went out to dinner they chatted with their friends, leaving only the enclosed space of the car for conversation.

"Yeah, in fact, I was just talkin' to Amos King," he said. "I did go, but it didn't do me any good. He knows he gave me the permission to do what I wanted, and he agrees that everything I did betters the community, but he still wants the second building stopped and torn down." He sighed, shook his head slowly, then, out of nowhere, started to chuckle.

"Oh my gosh," he said, adjusting himself, then took off his visor to rub his newly balder head. "When I was there at Bill's, his wife served us lemonade. And because of this medicine I'm takin', I get real emotional, like, whenever anyone's nice to me. So when she served me the lemonade, I started tearin' up. It was embarrassing!"

After a couple more calls his phone died. For quite a while afterward he said nothing and stared out the window as the farms gave way to houses, then to apartment complexes. Entering the city seemed to put Johnny's mind on a different path, away from the mule-plowed fields, the horses and buggies, and the people who owned them. Finally, in a tone tinged with hope and regret, he spoke: "It'll be real interesting to see what the doctor says today, you know? Like, if the chemo's workin'."

For a moment the cab of the Ford Focus was silent. Patti broke in: "I think it's working because that lump you had on your chest has gone down a lot!"

"Oh, yeah!" Johnny said, touching the shrunken mass near his collarbone. "I know it is; I can feel these tingles in my chest and legs and stuff, like the Good Guys are goin' 'round cleanin' out the Bad Guys."

"I also think we need to ask him which one of your medications is making you so constipated," Patti said, then took her eyes off the road briefly to turn to her daughter with a look of disgust. "I had to give him an enema the other night."

"Oh yeah. It was bad!" Johnny added, almost laughing.

"He hadn't been able to… you know… *go* in days," Patti said, "so he was getting really worried because-"

"Because that's how Frankie's brother died," Johnny interrupted and took over the story.

"From constipation?" Audra asked, her eyes wide.

"Yeah, but he was a real asshole. He wouldn't go to the

doctor and lived alone. So I'm gettin' real nervous about that, so your mom went to the drugstore and got an enema, and she's tryin' to help me—and I'm probably not bein' real nice—and-"

"I told him if he didn't stop yelling at me, I wasn't going to help him," Patti interjected, annoyed just remembering the scene.

"Yeah, and so we're strugglin' and we got it in and I finally went and, oh my God!" He lifted his once bushy eyebrows, crinkling his forehead with the whites around his eyes clearly visible. "I looked in the toilet, and I couldn't believe something that big came out of me. I mean, it was *huge*! It was as big as Jared!" he exclaimed, referencing his six-year-old grandson. He chuckled over the story for a few beats longer then let out a long sigh.

"So I'm real interested in what the doc says about it, that's all. You know, because if the treatment's not workin', what do we do then?" He sighed again and seemed to be talking to himself since no one else had said a word. "So, we'll see. Yeah. But I think it's workin'." He exhaled deeply one more time and looked out the window for a few more silent moments. "I tell ya. Everywhere I go people tell me they're prayin' for me. We'll know at this appointment if it's workin'."

***

"Hello," Dr. Caruso said with a slight nod, greeting the family as he stepped into the small medical room where the nurse had led them and sat on the stool. "First off, how are you feeling?" He looked straight at his patient with intense interest.

"I'm feeling great!" Johnny said, nearly jumping out of his seat. "I love that chemo stuff, Doc. I can feel it tinglin' in my chest like the Good Guys are battling the Bad Guys, and I'm thinkin' that's the chemo workin'," Johnny said, looking to the doctor for confirmation.

"Yes, that's the chemo working," he nodded and chuckled imperceptibly. "The Bad Guys, to use your analogy, are dying and that's why you feel the tingling."

"And also that thing on his chest has gone down," Patti pointed out.

"Oh. May I feel your chest?" he asked as he stood up to take a couple steps toward his patient who was perched on the tall paper-covered, table.

"You want to feel my chest, Doc? Isn't that a little forward? I mean, we just met...," Johnny joked. The young doctor chuckled, audibly this time, and instructed Johnny to lay back, then pressed on the spot where the mini-marshmallow sized lump had been.

"Wow!" he exclaimed, his face brightening with an actual smile as he pressed on other nearby spots. "This has shrunken significantly...Wow... I can barely feel where it was," he said, continuing to press. He felt a few more places then thoughtfully returned to his stool, in obvious awe. The doctor looked at his computer for a moment to gather his thoughts before delivering the preliminary results the family couldn't wait to hear.

"As I've explained before, there is a marker in prostate cancer called the PSA. It stands for prostate specific antigen. Generally, if that marker goes up it's bad, and conversely, going down is good. Healthy men will have a count of four or less," he paused to make sure the faces staring back at him were understanding his information. "People get worried when their count goes from six to seven. We doctors get quite concerned with a count of 100, OK?" He looked around the room again to all three heads nodding.

He took a deep breath and continued: "Frankly, your PSA starting number was the highest I've ever seen. I have seen 1,000 a few times before and I've *heard* of 3,000." He paused again as if even he couldn't believe the number wasn't a mistake. "Your PSA, as you know, started at over 22,000.

"However," Dr. Caruso continued, "You've also had the biggest percentage drop I've ever seen. You're now down to 9,800, which is a 55% drop. That's... that's quite remarkable."

"Yes!" Johnny said, raising his fists in triumph. Patti sighed and loosened her brow in relief.

The doctor put up a hand as if to quiet the premature

celebration. "But don't get too hung up on the numbers," he warned. "What is really significant here is what I *didn't* feel on your chest a few minutes ago. If that lump were still there and the numbers had dropped like they did, I wouldn't be as encouraged. If the lump had disappeared and the number hadn't dropped, I'd still be encouraged. So, it's the physical evidence and how you feel that is most important. Since the lump is gone *and* the numbers have dropped so dramatically *and* you're feeling good, it's an extremely positive sign."

"Well, Doc," Johnny said, happier than he'd been for a month, "I tell ya, I gotta lotta people prayin' for me!"

"I'd say that's probably as good as anything I can do for you," he replied.

Johnny was all smiles as they filed into the big, busy chemo dispensing room with nurses bustling back and forth from the armchairs filled with pallid-looking patients to computers on the counters by the walls. They led the beaming family to an empty set of chairs with Patti and Audra at Johnny's sides.

"Right or left—do you have a preference?" the nurse asked with syringe in hand.

"Oh—I got my port installed," the patient said, pulling back his shirt and revealing the bandages. "Is Lisa here today? Man, she's good at finding blood. She's so good at finding blood, she must be part vampire!"

The nurses within earshot giggled. "No, she's off this week. She's probably on a beach somewhere."

"Oh, must be why she wasn't there to draw my blood on Sunday. This other lady wasn't quite as good," he said, revealing the badly bruised underside of his right arm, making the nurses frown. "Lisa just put it in my hand. Why couldn't the other lady do that?"

While the nurse drew blood from his port, she explained about the different needle sizes used, then prepared to hook up the IV. Audra, sitting to her father's right, watched the process closely as Patti sat silently on the other side, looking at her phone.

Johnny turned to his daughter. "I was hopin' you'd get to meet Lisa," he said in disappointment. "She's cool." He reminded

113

her that she was the one who recognized him in the parking lot after only meeting him once.

"Can you feel the chemo going through you?" Audra asked.

"Yeah, I can. It's really weird. Later I'll feel tingly here and there, like in my lungs where a lot of the Bad Guys are, and all the way down to my feet."

"What do you think about when you're sitting here for an hour?"

"He's usually on his phone," Patti answered for him. "Remember the pictures?" She had taken a picture of his first chemo session, and one in post-op after getting his port, both times with a phone stuck to his ear. This time his phone had died on the ride up.

"Well, what are you thinking about now?"

"Oh, just all the things I have to do this afternoon. Since you'll be riding around with me today, we're going to meet Grace for lunch at the restaurant in town. I told her you wanted to meet her."

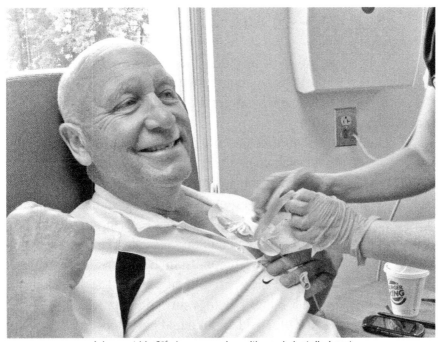

Johnny at his 2nd chemo session with newly installed port.

After the session Patti insisted they drop her off at home and take her car to Amishland since it had air conditioning. Johnny didn't argue, and they left for Bart, first calling Grace with his newly charged phone, making sure she'd be willing to have lunch after hours since she got off at noon on Fridays and they wouldn't be able to get to Georgetown before then. She graciously accepted. Johnny told her he had some really good news to share but wouldn't tell her what it was over the phone.

The lush, green scenery enveloped the travelers as they made their way to Lancaster County. To the left and the right, life abounded with the sounds of insects buzzing about and the sweet smell of flowers wafting through the air. Birds circled fields looking for prey. Trees hung over the roads in spots, their full leaves providing cooling shade. Teen boys in straw hats and suspenders led teams of horses over fields; young girls in plain dresses picked the fields of strawberries, placing them carefully in large boxes to sell.

Johnny parked at Hometown Kitchen and, even before he reached the door, people with and without long beards stopped to say hello. Inside the small but airy cafe-like restaurant and deli with an open kitchen to the left, groups of Amish and English alike filled the busy dining area. Amish and Mennonite waitresses with black aprons and white bonnets bustled around, taking orders and bringing food, while happy conversations floated through the fresh baked bread-scented air.

After greeting a few other patrons, Johnny chose one of the only open tables and sat by his daughter facing the door as they waited for his work wife to arrive. Within minutes, she walked through the door, the inspector made the introductions, and they all sat down together. Eagerly, the older woman turned her attention to her co-worker and pleaded with concerned and serious eyes: "Tell me you have good news."

Johnny relayed the story of the encouraging improvement. Overjoyed to tears, Grace's eyes welled up, causing Johnny's eyes to well up, too.

"Now, don't you go blubberin' on me!" Grace teased and wagged her finger at him. She turned to Audra. "I tell everyone my zoning officer is going through menopause." The younger woman giggled.

Abe Stoltzfus, the owner of The Hometown Kitchen, and Dan Stoltzfus's business partner and Mennonite cousin, walked over to the table. "Hallo John. How are you doing today?"

"How can I not be doing good, man? I just had a bag of chemo this morning. That stuff is awesome!" Johnny said. Abe chuckled.

"You just missed your chance!" Grace playfully scolded her zoning officer, puzzling him. "You should have said, 'I'm about to have lunch with two beautiful women. How could I not be doing good?' "

Everyone laughed. Johnny shared the news that the chemo was working—and dramatically.

"I also wanted to say sorry again about the other day," Abe said uncomfortably, crossing his arms over his pin striped button down shirt tucked into jeans. " I had no idea they were actually interviewing you."

"Oh, man!" Johnny laughed. "Are you kiddin'? That's now one of my best stories. I laughed about that so hard!" He slapped the table and threw his head back.

Audra asked what happened. Grace, of course, had already heard.

"Well, I had to meet with these two detectives, so I come in here with them and they have coats and ties on. And I shout across the place, I go, 'Abe. Can you believe it? I'm walkin' in with guys with coats and ties on!' "

"See? This is why people love your dad," Grace interjected with admiring eyes.

"And Abe goes, 'Oh yeah, that's really somethin'. And we sit at a table and I say to the detectives, I say, 'He owns the place, and he also built the house that you're here about.' See, this crazy English guy had this idea that the township poisoned the water and is now covering it up," he explained knowing Audra would ask. "And I said to them, 'You gotta understand. Everybody's friends here. Everybody gets along. It's not a problem.' "

"So here comes Abe over to the table—and he didn't know they were detectives: 'You guys interviewin' him? You know you can't believe anything he says!' " Johnny slapped the table and threw his head back again for a big cackle while Audra covered her mouth and widened her eyes at the gaffe. "So, of course, after the interview I immediately went through to the construction company side to tell Dan, and we laughed and laughed."

Abe sheepishly apologized again and thanked God for the good news that the treatment was working. He left the table to spread the word.

Audra asked her father why he hadn't mentioned the story with detectives before. It sounded so exciting.

"I don't know," he answered with a shrug. "It's all just a day in the life here."

When asked why they were questioning him, Johnny and Grace explained about the situation with the town "wacko" who'd had this theory about the town's water for a few years and would occasionally even call the schools to warn them about it. In his latest episode, he put up 4x8 sheets of plywood on a piece of property that he owned in another township that said, "Bart township criminal acts, Grace Hostetter. Call the district attorney." A second smaller board hung below with "Grace Hostetter lied to the police" written on it. Officials finally interviewed Grace about it a month earlier—and now Johnny—to see if there was any truth to his claims.

After the last chuckles, they talked business, including whether or not Leon Stoltzfus's move into his new building warranted a hearing.

"I don't think we need one because there was fiberglass manufacturing there before," the zoning officer reasoned. "Now, of course, it was a different *kind* of fiberglass manufacturing that was there before, but I don't think that matters. Manufacturing is manufacturing."

Grace nodded then her eyes suddenly lit up. "Oh, I do have something good to tell you," she said and slapped the table. "We

117

only have Gabriel's hearing this month." Johnny was glad to get it over with.

"Can I get you all anything else?" the Amish waitress asked and reached for the empty plates on the table. After the diners declined more and expressed their satisfaction with lunch, she turned to the inspector. "How are you doin', John?"

The inspector told her the good news, which she was also glad to hear. "You know, John, you have to let us help you!"

"That's right!" Grace chimed in.

"No, no, no, no," Johnny said, shaking his head vigorously, refusing help of any kind.

"Yes, John, you do," she insisted, making it clear that she wasn't going to take "no" for an answer.

Johnny excused himself to the bathroom and heard Grace gushing to his daughter: "He's just the most awesome individual." His eyes misted again. On the way back to the table, he stopped to pay for the meal and another waitress asked him about his health. After he filled her in, she asked him if he'd do her a favor. "I'd love to," he said and gave her a hug.

Johnny returned to the table with a big smile splashed across his face and a story on the tip of his tongue. "See the girl that just took my money?" he asked, pointing with his eyes. "You know Levi Fisher of Fisher's Housewares? That's his daughter. Anyway, she wants me to go over to her house to see her mother because her mother's the one who has been diagnosed with stage four lung cancer. And she said, 'If you see John Coldiron have him stop by and see me.' "

"Awwww!" Grace and Audra said in unison.

"Now, that's nice," Johnny nodded. "And I told her, 'I'll go. I was also diagnosed with cancer, and we can have some things to talk about.' "

"That's probably why she wanted you to stop—'cause she heard," Grace said. "But you see, isn't that awesome?"

Johnny smiled and sighed happily. "That's being a part of the community. So, anyway, I got another job to do: Number Nine, Lancaster Avenue!" He laughed, "But I like doin' those jobs. And it's right by Antique's place, so we'll stop and see him on the way."

***

Johnny parked beside the Antique store and waited for the owner to notice. Black buggies, pulled by bay and chestnut morgans and saddlebreds, jangled by on the blistering hot, not yet summer day. Finally, the bishop emerged to greet them.

"Hey man. You sellin' any Antiques?"

"Oh, no. No one wants to go in that stuffy place on a day like this!" Antique said with a grin, ducking his head into the driver side window. "I didn't recognize your car."

"It's my wife's," he explained and started again in his big teasing voice: "My daughter here said she couldn't leave Georgetown unless she saw Antique!"

"Oh, you were the one, John," he volleyed. "You're just blamin' it on her!"

Johnny cackled at the exchange for a long moment. "I just had my second round of chemo!" he announced, practically shouting, still sitting in the car.

The bishop asked how it was going. Johnny told him that everything the doctors were doing for him was working: his "bad blood count" was down 60% and he felt great. "The first one didn't make me sick, and I asked my oncologist about that today and he said that normally whatever your reaction is for the first one, is what you'll do," Johnny explained, hoping that would remain true for the next four.

"Mrs. Fisher just had her second one yesterday," Antique informed in a serious tone and concerned eyes. "My wife went to see her. She's handling it, but it's hard for her."

"I know," Johnny said. "We were up at The Hometown Kitchen and her daughter just asked me to see her today, so that's where I'm headed." A feeling of fortune swept over him as he got out of the car and walked a couple houses over to the Fisher's, crossing the tiny green lawns by the road on the way. Audra stayed behind to tour the store and ask Antique some questions about her father.

119

Inspection stop

Johnny riding around Bart

CHAPTER 14

Late June

Johnny, flying high, buzzed like a bee from house to house collecting checks and dropping off permits. Things were going great: the treatment was working, *he* was still working, and Young John was working more by covering the inspections he couldn't get to because of his doctor appointments. His son had actually even started to talk about getting a tractor to cut the weeds in the pasture like his father, J.R., always had. Even the dreaded hearing with Gabriel over the Nickel Mines debacle was rescheduled for the next month.

Five days later his spirits soared even higher after another appointment with another steep drop in his PSA. He started to think maybe he would live forever after all and stopped at his mother's to tell her the exciting news. "I just saw the Doc," Johnny reported, the ecstasy palpable in his voice, "and my blood count is now down to three thousand! That's down from over 22,000 just four weeks ago." Johnny smiled with more pride than if had been asked to throw the ceremonial first ball at a Phillies' game.

Saturday he took his golfing grandsons to their lesson and worked on the playset. By Sunday he was completely exhausted. Despite his fatigue, he made it across the field with Patti to accept Brooke's invitation to lounge by the pool on the steamy-hot June day.

It was the longest day of the year, and one of Johnny's favorite out of all 365. That's how much he loved summer. He loved everything about it: baseball, golf, mowing, and even the heat. If he could move everyone, including the Amish, to Florida and have summer all year round, he would have done it long ago.

Not only was it the summer solstice, it was Father's Day, too. With his feet in the pool sitting in the shade beside his wife, they sipped on ice cold drinks that Dolly served and watched Brooke's children, Wyatt and his younger sister, Annabelle, splash around in the water. As a surprise Father's Day gift, Brooke presented him with three Phillies tickets—one for him, one for Patti, and the last for Wyatt, whose birthday was the day after the game.

Johnny loved baseball, once having had aspired to be a major league pitcher, and hadn't been to an actual major league game in so long he couldn't even remember the last time. He thanked his daughter and looked forward, through the tears welling up in his eyes, to Friday like an Amishman looks forward to visiting his Mennonite cousin to watch a game on TV.

***

"The Amish love baseball," Johnny said to his wife in the passenger seat of the little orange car as they drove to Philadelphia for the game. "They especially love the Phillies. I told you about the one guy, Mose, right? The one who went to Texas to play rock-and roll? He's in a wheelchair now?"

She said he had with a look of uncertainty on her face.

"Well, he told me about this one time a couple years ago when he went on vacation with his brother for the weekend and they rented a place. Him and his nephews love the Phillies—just love the Phillies. He said, 'John, we were havin' such a good time,' he said, 'We were there and me and the boys were watchin' the Phillies on the TV, and we were hootin' and hollerin' and this and that, 'and the next morning,' he said, 'my sister-in-law came in and told them that was the end of that and there will be no more watching of the Phillies, and that she would not tolerate it!'"

Johnny looked over at his wife who hadn't heard this story and was interested in the husband and wife dynamic. "I looked at Mose, and I said, 'Excuse me?' I said, 'Now, Mose, I'm tellin' ya

122

right now what I'da done if I'da been your brother. I'da said, you got two alternatives here. Either your bed goes outside or me and the guys are goin' down to the local bar and we're gonna watch the Phillies there!' " Johnny stopped to cackle at his own joke; Patti kept her negative knee-jerk reaction to herself. "And Mose goes, 'Oh no, no. We just decided we could do without.' " He paused to shake his head and take a deep breath.

"How are you doin' back there, bud?" he asked Wyatt who sat in the backseat entranced by a video game on his iPad. "Are you excited to see the Phillies?" He said he was. Patti said she was also.

"Me, too! I can't wait to tell Reuben about this—he's the quadriplegic Amish architect," he said, reminding his wife who nodded though she didn't remember. "He works with Mose. He's a big Phillies fan. I'll go in their office to drop something off and say something like, 'They've lost four in a row. I'm goin' up there to straighten them out!' " He laughed at his own quote.

At the game they found their seat and bought the hot dogs when the man came around shouting, "Hot dogs! Get your hot dogs!" They passed their cash over to the end of the row again when another guy came around for "Soda!" and "Popcorn!" Patti took a picture to post on Facebook, and the three watched the game—even Wyatt who had to leave his iPad in the car.

As they watched the Phillies give up run after run to the Washington Nationals, Johnny reminisced about his childhood baseball years. He had so desperately wanted to be in the major leagues, that he practiced for hours and hours after school and on the weekends, throwing balls as hard as he could at a wooden plank against the house his dad set up. In high school he was a star pitcher, managing to throw balls 90 miles per hour, and scoring a couple of no-hitters. When an injury ended his pitching career, he repurposed himself as a catcher. He always wondered what his life would have been like if that hadn't happened.

"Well, that was fun even though they lost, huh?" Patti said, her hands on the steering wheel, her eyes on the road.

"Yeah, that was," Johnny said, hoping that their loss, which ended their winning streak, didn't foretell misfortune for him, too.

"It was nice of Brooke to buy the tickets, wasn't it?"

"Yeah," Patti agreed. "I'm sorry you had to get sick to make Brooke nicer."

That thought had crossed his mind, but he decided to just enjoy the rekindled relationship with his middle daughter. He sighed and suddenly remembered about the surgery his buddy, Frank, had on his shoulder that day. He had completely forgotten to call. Unable to find a pen or paper to write it down, he made a mental note to call the next day. He couldn't believe something like that slipped his mind. It wasn't like him.

Johnny and Wyatt at the Phillies' game (photo by Patti Coldiron).

***

The next day he remembered to call Frank and promised to stop by on his way back from the practice range where he wanted to take Wyatt and Zander for some extra golf ball hitting practice. Patti and Annabelle came along, too. Frank, happy to see his friend, sat on his plush, white couch with his arm in a sling, while his wife, Aileen, fussed over him.

On the way from the Parrishes, they passed Ruth's landscaped cottage, surprised to see his mother digging in her flowerbeds at a time she would usually be at church. Johnny slammed on the brakes and doubled back to see what was wrong.

"Oh, I just wasn't feelin' good this morning," she bemoaned.

Johnny admitted he wasn't feeling his best either and rhetorically asked, "Why do you think that is?" Shaking her head sadly, Ruth said she didn't know, though she did. They both knew the answer.

"I know why," Patti piped up, trying to be helpful. "It's because you're eighty-four, and he's got cancer!"

***

A couple sunny days later, Johnny's buddies invited him to another round of free golf. He happily accepted.

"So this one time I drove 'em up to their camp—that's what they call their place in the mountains," Johnny continued after Huston took the first shot, "and this is the summer before last, and Liz, Dan's wife, is there with the older daughters who are, like, twenty, twenty-two, that are married, and she has another who is, like, eighteen. All the guys were gonna play golf, and I said to Liz, I says, 'Well, what are all you females gonna do while we're gone?' And she said, 'Oh, while yous are gone we're probably gonna sunbathe out in the yard.' I said, 'That's OK, boys. I don't need to go play golf!' " The five men laughed at the story as they selected their clubs from the bags in the backs of the carts.

"Hey, how's Frank?" Huston asked, walking to the first tee.

"He's doin' real good. I went over to see him Sunday on my

125

way back from takin' the kids to the golf lesson. I asked him how he was and he was like, 'I don't want you askin' me how I am!' " Johnny quoted, nearly screamed as he remembered Frank doing. "He says, 'I'm the one who asks *you* how you are!' " Johnny laughed. "But he's fine. Of course, now, Aileen's not gonna let him even lift that arm for months!"

The men stood in a circle as Huston tossed the tee up into the air and it landed on the grass, pointing to Johnny's loafers.

"Hey, J.D. Why don't you shoot from the women's tees?" Huston suggested. "It'll be easier, and it'll make it more fun." The rest of the men nodded in agreement.

"You don't understand, guys," Johnny said, feeling insulted but knew they were just trying to help. "I have to have a challenge. I have to have somethin' to work for. You can't take my fight from me!" He set up and took his shot from the men's tees.

They continued on through the course on the beautiful summer morning. There on the golf course with his friends, the sun glinting off the metal clubs, the birds chirping, the gentle breeze blowing, and the sun warming his weakened body, he felt at at peace. He imagined God smiling down on him, healing him with his breath whenever he felt the warm wind cross his now balder head. He realized it didn't matter if he played well; what mattered was that he got well.

"It was nice to put a face to the name," Davy Huston said about running into Grace and Chester at the Bullfrog Inn some weeks ago and laughed about Grace mentioning the U-Haul story.

"Oh, I've got an *Amish* U-Haul story," Johnny said as he lined up his putt. "This is a good one. We had a waitress at the Hometown Kitchen up there, who is a good looking Amish girl—and most of them are not—but she was a very attractive Amish girl, and it was the summer before. My friend, Dan, who runs the construction company side, they said, 'Did you hear what happened to Esther?' 'No,' I said. He goes, 'Esther went down to the beach,' and they went down and stayed, I guess a week, or a few days, her and some other kids, and their driver towed a U-Haul trailer. Anyway, the guy came and he picked up the U-Haul and took it back while the girls were still at the beach in their bathing suits," he cracked up, "so they had to go home in their bathing suits to their Amish families!"

"I would've liked to have seen that!" Huston said and took his shot which landed in the hole.

"And, of course, Esther—I know her mom and dad," Johnny continued with a chuckle. "I go in to eat at the restaurant, and I go, 'Ha, ha, boy, Esther, I wish I'd been at the beach!' She goes, 'What?' I said, 'I heard about the clothes.' She goes, 'I don't want to talk about it. I don't know anything.' " Johnny laughed again and finally made his ball in the hole.

"Of course, I've kidded her enough now when she sees me comin' she's just smiling' from ear to ear. I've had drivers tell me, like, they have taken a carload of girls to the beach and drop them out, and they've got the long dresses, they've got the coverings, you know, and one goes, 'John,' he said, 'I'm telling you right now, the next thing I know, I realized I didn't know where we were meetin',' he says, 'and I'm walking down the boardwalk and I'm right behind six girls and they are speakin' Dutch, and they don't have any clothes on, and I realize those were the girls I brought!' He goes, 'Boy, was I shocked!' " Johnny laughed and cackled, slapping his leg after climbing into the cart with Huston.

As they finished up the round, one of the golfers asked if he had felt any ill effects from the chemo; he swore he hadn't and hoped his hair falling out would be the worst of it. The next day was to be his third chemo session and the first since it was changed to Wednesdays in Kennett Square, much closer to their home.

Kennett Square was the town where Johnny had attended high school and played baseball, and was inducted into their local baseball hall of fame. During his acceptance speech after thanking everyone for remembering him and expressing his deep honor of being inducted, there on stage with a microphone in his hand and a captive audience, he couldn't resist telling a story.

"One day I was at a golf course in Oxford, and this was about twenty years ago, and I'm there with the most famous local golfer that ever played: Blaise Giroso. Now, whenever I golfed with him people would just follow him around and watch. He was that good.

This one time we were at Wyncote and this old guy is following us all around the course just starin'. I said to Blaise, I said, 'Man, doesn't that get old?' He said, 'No, you get used to it.'

"So we finish playin' and we were in the parking lot puttin' our clubs back in our cars, and this same guy drives by real slow and shouts, 'Hey!' and I'm like, 'Geez, can't he leave Blaise alone?' Blaise turns around and the guy goes, 'No, not you. The other guy!' I'm like, 'Huh?' He goes, 'Are you Johnny Coldiron?' I go, 'Yeah!' He goes, 'I used to watch you play baseball. You were one hell of a player!'" The speech nearly brought the house down.

As the party of five added up the scores, Ronnie, a tall man a few years older than Johnny, asked about his health and what was next for him.

"Tomorrow's my third chemo session and that's when I get my new blood count. It's so fun to hear that number drop and see how excited my doctor gets."

"Hey J.D.," Ronnie said as they returned their carts and walked through the parking lot, golf bags in tow, "you know at that last hole when you could have made that shot for the birdie to beat me?"

"Yeah?"

"I wanted you to make it," he confessed, "but you'da had to kill me before I would have admitted it!"

CHAPTER 15

Early July

Johnny and Patti took the elevator to the second floor of the Kennett Square Penn Medical Center for his third chemo session. Upon entering the small waiting room that looked identical to the last one in West Chester with the same thin, green carpet and the same manila walls, Patti took a seat. The patient limped over to the receptionist behind the glass to announce his arrival. The thirty-something brown haired woman slid the window open and flashed a friendly smile.

"Hi there. I'm Johnny Coldiron, and I have an 8:00 appointment with Dr. Caruso," he said in his booming voice, always unaware of his volume.

"Hello, Mr. Coldiron. You're an early bird, aren't ya?" the woman teased in her Philadelphia accent. It was not yet 8:00 am, and she hadn't planned on starting yet. "Is this your first time here?"

He explained that it was his first time at that particular office, though not his first chemo session, and described the Penn Medical Cancer Center tour he'd been on.

"I'm Paula. Nice to meet you, Mr. C.," she said as he sat down in the closest chair to her. "So what do you do for a living?" She shuffled papers around at her desk while making conversation with the new patient.

"I'm a building inspector and work up in Lancaster County, mostly with the Amish."

"No kiddin'!" she said, and told him her cousin lived in Paradise, PA. "I bet your job is interesting!"

He told her the actual job was dull, but the stories he got from working with the Amish were worth it. "Yeah. And I've done inspections in these Amish houses that were so spectacular they looked all English except they didn't have electric. See, they are supposed to be the Plain People, so anything fancy is, like, heresy or somethin'," Johnny explained and adjusted himself in his chair. "This one time I looked at the Amish lady whose house I was inspecting, and I said, 'This is just spectacular. My only question is, where's the electric?' She looked at me and said, 'Well… do you want to see my microwave oven?' "

"No kidding! They have microwaves? How do you run a microwave without electricity?"

"They have propane generators. But believe me, they have everything they want to have. Now, it wasn't like that when I first started there nine years ago."

"Is that right?" She smiled and checked the next person in while listening.

"Oh yeah. They have everything: computers, smart phones. There's no difference. Like I tell my bishop all the time, 'The only difference between me and you is that you wear a uniform!' " Johnny stopped to laugh at his recurring joke. "But they know as soon as those conveniences of TVs and computers become commonplace, it will drastically change the home life from what they have now, and that is what they—meaning the bishops—fight against. They want to keep the home social-based among people instead of among those things like computers with the social media. I tell ya, social media is gonna be the downfall of society!"

"Oh really?" she said with a half smirk, quite entertained by this new patient. "Why don't you like social media?"

"I don't know. I just don't like it. You should be talking to real people, not people on computers!"

Just then a nurse in scrubs with a clipboard in hand appeared at the open door to the office, and called out his name.

***

After Johnny's vitals were taken, Dr. Caruso popped in to see if he had any new questions or concerns (which he didn't), checked on the lump on his chest (which had completely disappeared), then left as quickly as he came. Johnny and Patti were ushered into the now familiar room for the IV that looked identical to the one in Exton and West Chester except instead of olive chairs for the patients, they were cream-colored. While hooked up, he realized the doctor didn't give him his new PSA level and asked the nurse about it.

"That's odd," she said, tapping a few keys on the laptop, panning through his digital chart. "They didn't do that for you this time." After a few more taps she involuntarily gasped. "Oh my goodness. You're at 3,000?"

"Yeah," Johnny said with a chuckle, soaking up the attention, "but look where I started."

The nurse's jaw dropped. "This can't be right," she said reading 22,282 displayed on her screen then saw his next number. "Wow, that's a huge drop, too!" The nurse, her jaw still unhinged, marveled at Johnny as he sat in the chemo chair wearing a white visor, white golfing shirt, black shorts, and a smile. He was oddly proud of the fact that he had the highest PSA anyone had ever heard of, and maybe the highest in the history of prostate cancer based on everyone's reactions. "You are, like, the poster child for how chemo is supposed to work!" the nurse proclaimed.

During the hour long drip, Patti took another picture of her husband on his phone and posted it to Facebook. Because he had nothing new to report, he didn't bother calling anyone with an update. Afterward, Patti dropped him off at home, and in the cab of his truck he made out his list of things to do for the day. On the way to Bart he got some troubling news.

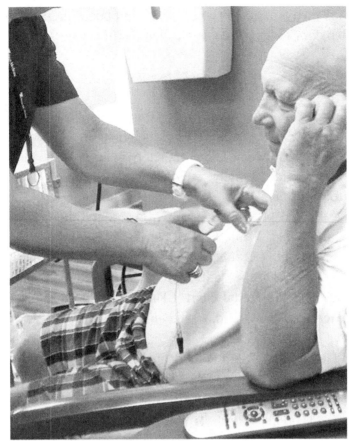

Johnny conducting business during his 3rd chemo session (photo by Patti Coldiron)

***

The zoning officer walked through the door of the township building with a long face. When Grace saw him she went pale and her worry lines deepened.

"Hey Grace," the zoning officer said with much less enthusiasm than his usually highly caffeinated morning persona.

"John, what's wrong?" she asked, unable to wait for his story.

"I just found out a golfing buddy of mine died. His funeral is Tuesday."

"Oh, no!" she said, relieved it wasn't to do with his own health. "It's not Frank or Huston, is it?" Though she had met them only once very briefly at the Bullfrog Inn, she felt like they were her own friends due to all of the golfing stories her co-worker had told her over the years starring the pair.

"No, no. It was Carl Fretz who ran the People's Bank of Oxford. We golfed every now and then, and we even owned a racehorse together about twenty-five years ago."

Grace wanted to ask what he died of but couldn't bring herself to do it in case he said cancer. She didn't want to hear about anyone else with cancer, and especially anyone dying from it. "Had he been sick?"

"I don't know. I saw him a couple months ago. He was in his right mind but was using a walker. He was eighty-five."

"Oh. Well, he lived a long life."

"Yeah," Johnny said with sad eyes, thinking about his own future. Once he thought he'd live forever. Now he felt like if he died at sixty-five like his father, he would feel fortunate. "My mom is turning eighty-five next week."

"Oh, is she? I enjoyed meetin' her when she drove around with you. She seems like a great lady, and I know you love her. Are you throwin' her a party?"

He explained that he wasn't, but his sister was. He then quickly changed the subject and asked if she had anything he needed to take care of.

"Nope. I'm taking a half day today. Chester's meetin' me here in a few minutes, and I'm takin' him to the doctor."

Johnny, alarmed, asked what was wrong. She assured him it was probably nothing, but he hadn't been feeling 100%, and they were just going for a check-up. "At 76, you can't be too cautious, you know?"

As Bart's zoning officer walked out the door, Chester was just pulling in the parking lot to meet his wife for lunch first.

"Hey Chester. How are you, man?" he reached out to shake his hand. "Grace says you haven't been feelin' so hot."

"Oh, I'm fine," Chester said. "She's the one that's worried. How are you doin'? Grace tells me your treatments are really workin'."

"Yeah. Yeah. It's been really amazing. My bad blood count—

which the doctor couldn't even believe because it started so high—it's gone down, like, 70% since they started me on everything," said Johnny, proudly.

Chester nodded with a smile. "That's what I hear!"

"Yeah, my doctor can hardly believe it. He's this young kid and it's so cool to see how excited he gets—he practically bounces around the room. I said to him, I said, 'Doc, I've got a lot of people prayin' for me.' He goes, 'Oh, that's better than anything I can do for you!'"

"Well, we're prayin' for you, too, John."

"I know, I know, and I appreciate it. I tell ya, this area is just so different. Everywhere I go around here people tell me the same thing. 'We're prayin' for ya, we're prayin' for ya.' I'm practically in one big prayer service the whole time I'm here. I'm just afraid that..." he paused to pick just the right words. He didn't want to sound like he believed that being around all these people who were praying for him was responsible for bringing him back from the brink of death, but wasn't it obvious? Even the doctor practically said so himself. "I would hate to have to leave, is all."

"John, are you still worryin' about Bill?" he asked. "I told you. You're not going anywhere as long as I have anything to do about it. Hasn't Grace told you, you have bigger fish to fry?"

"Oh, no, no, no. I'm not worried," pretended Johnny. "I'm... I'm just anxious to get my new blood count again since they didn't give me one this morning. I really like those counts because it's lettin' me know that it's workin'."

Chester wished him luck, then Johnny climbed back into his pickup and sped away to the next inspection on his list

***

While driving back from the church Tuesday morning, buried deep in thought, he almost didn't hear his phone ring. That funeral, more than any other he could remember, affected him so significantly he couldn't even cry. He couldn't help but imagine himself inside the coffin or what the people who stood in front of everyone would say

134

about him. As he had listened to the eulogy he remembered the one he gave at his father's funeral and wondered who would give his. Huston? Frank? Young John?

It was Audra calling. She had called to check up on him and asked why he sounded so glum. He explained that he had just attended Carl Fretz's funeral and hadn't gotten his mother a birthday present yet for the party that night.

"So you are going?" Audra asked.

"I guess so," he said with a tired sigh. "I'll call you tomorrow when I get my new numbers."

The hours that followed passed slowly and were filled with reflection. Though he tried not to think about the world without him, he couldn't keep his brain from the subject. Even imagining mowing a giant lawn—one of his favorite things to do—didn't help. The inspector crossed a few more names off his list and managed to find a suitable present for his mother, but didn't feel like joking or pretending to be happy. He just wanted to be alone; he dreaded going to the party where, if he weren't happy, his mom would worry even more (if that were possible).

Nevertheless, back at home he wrapped the presents. While doing so, he decided to just make an appearance at the party to drop off the gifts. He called Brooke to tell her he wasn't going after all, asked her to tell Wyatt and Annabelle he was sorry that he couldn't take them, and drove to his mother's house. When he got there on that steamy summer evening the place was empty, but he heard children across the giant lawn, playing and splashing in his sister's pool. Without anyone knowing he'd come, he set the presents on her kitchen table and left.

***

The next morning he drove alone to his checkup appointment in Kennett with Dr. Caruso through the rain. Already feeling down and disappointed in himself for not walking over to the pool where he'd seen everybody the night before (and probably worrying his mother to death), the dreary weather only compounded his mood. When mixed with self-pity, everything brewed inside of him and made him feel even worse the more he dwelt on it. But, he figured, once Dr. Caruso gave him the new PSA, he would have something positive to hold on to. That would lift his spirits.

"Hey Doc! I need your home phone number!" he said, mustering a happy, jokey attitude if just for a moment. "When I didn't get new numbers last week, everybody thought I was withholding information!"

The doctor chuckled at his patient's way of putting things and informed him that he was only going to get PSA levels every month now. He also reminded him not to get too hung up on the numbers. "What's important is that the cancer is not growing, and so far, so good."

Johnny admitted the last chemo treatment a week earlier had left him drained, and that this morning he was feeling as low on energy as he ever had. After a nurse drew another vial of blood, the inspector hurried back to his truck through the rain and disappointment, eager to get to Amishland, only to discover a dead battery. In his scrambled state of mind, he had left the lights on. Tired, angry, and sad, he called his son to come jump him, half expecting him to still be in bed.

The patient sat in his truck, unable to get on with things, almost giving into despair when Audra called. He knew she was calling for his new PSA number and didn't want to answer, but did anyway. He told her he didn't get one again, and there wouldn't be another one for a month. His voice was so uncharacteristically negative she asked him what was wrong. He explained about the dead battery and the birthday party he almost attended, but not what was really bothering him. For the first time he had started to think that the Bad Guys might win after all. What if they did?

Putting on a happy voice, he called his mom to tell her there was no news today and got off the phone before she asked about the night before. He felt the volcano of frustration boiling inside of him ready to erupt at any moment, and spewing it on her just might kill her. So when his son came to rescue him, he vented; Young John stayed cool and said nothing.

Johnny raced away as quickly as his truck would allow with no time for thank yous or goodbyes and sped toward Amishland. There he would feel better. Unable to see clearly through the driving rain, he almost hit several buggies on the way when they popped up out of nowhere as he flew over the hills.

At the Bart Township Building, he stomped through the door, pushing all his negative feelings aside to put on a happy face for Grace. The inspector stopped short when her face did not match his.

"Grace, what's the matter?" he asked with alarmed concern. His brow furrowed and his pulse quickened remembering something about a doctor's appointment the day before. "Is it Chester?"

She couldn't speak and burst into tears. He stood in stunned silence and waited for the details, suddenly forgetting his own troubles.

Johnny Coldiron and "Grace" outside Hometown Kitchen, June 2015

CHAPTER 16

Mid July

"Oh, John, they found a mass on his pancreas," she cried, breaking down.

"Oh my God. Is it…?" He stopped, not wanting to even utter the word when it came to Chester, but the meaning was clear.

"We don't know yet, but his mother died of pancreatic cancer when she was 78."

After she told him everything the doctor had said, Johnny hugged her for so long she started crying again. He released his embrace and stepped back to look at her, his hands squeezing her shoulders.

"Let's just assume it's not… you know… and we'll pray, 'cause I'm tellin' ya what, prayers work. Look at me!" He slapped both hands to his chest. "I should be dead right now!" he said in his loudest, silliest voice to get her to stop crying. It worked. Her tears dried and she smiled at her friend who had a way of putting things.

***

The next week was a blur. Johnny worried about Chester but that only led to worrying about himself. Chester was the one keeping him in his zoning officer position and among the praying people who were keeping him alive. What if the unthinkable happened and Chester died?

That Saturday, Johnny, Frank, and Aileen took Patti to her favorite restaurant, Woody's in North East, Maryland, to celebrate her sixty-fourth birthday. Huston and Cheryl were away and couldn't join them. The hostess gathered up four menus, announced "Coldiron, party of four?" and led them to a table in the bright and spacious dining room.

"Oh man, we got some news about Chester the other day," Johnny said, shaking his head and taking a seat.

Just then the waitress came over to get their drink orders and left. Aileen asked about the news.

"Well, you remember Chester, right? He was the one I introduced you to at the... at the... geez!" he said, rubbing his head and squinting in frustration. "Why can't I remember the name of that place?"

"The Bullfrog Inn?" Aileen asked.

"Yes! Geez, this chemo brain," he said, shaking his head. "Anyway, they just found-"

"He has cancer," Patti blurted out, interrupting her husband's story and stealing his thunder. Johnny sighed.

Aileen gasped. "Oh, really?" she said, her brown eyes doubling in size. Frank leaned in to hear more.

"Well, no, Patti," Johnny corrected tersely and glared at his wife, who sat beside him, "they don't know if it's cancer. I was going to say that they just found a mass in his pancreas. I walked into the township building after having a bad couple-a days, and right away when I walked in the door and saw Grace, I could tell that there was su'um seriously the matter. She starts cryin' and I go, I says, 'Is it about Chester?' and she says, 'John, they found a mass on his pancreas and a...' oh, what's it called? A... a...," he stammered, interrupting his own story.

"Tumor?" Aileen offered.

"No... a..."

"Module?" Patti guessed.

"No, it's a funny lookin' word..."

"Polyp?" Frank said.

"Yeah, a polyp. Geez!" he said, banging his head with his hand a couple times, like the Fonz smacking the jukebox at Arnold's. "They found a polyp on his intestine, and I was like, 'Oh my God,' because stuff on your pancreas is no good," he said, lowering his head to look through his sparse eyebrows at his friends.

"I asked her, I said, 'Do they know anything yet?' and she goes, 'No, not yet but the MRI showed no additional tumors in the... in the abdomen, so that's good.' I asked her if they were gonna do a biopsy, and she said, 'Yeah, on the 22nd.' And he's also havin' some kind of ultrasound then, too. She said the doctor told 'em if the tumor hasn't gotten into the surrounding stuff, like the blood vessels, then they can do surgery to remove the tumor since it's on the tail end of the pancreas. She goes, 'We have an appointment set up to meet with the surgeon in August, so we are prayin' for that.' I'm like, 'I'm prayin' too, Grace. We can make it through this, don't you worry!' Then she said that the doctor told her that it doesn't mean... well, you know... that it's going to work. And then she goes, 'John, you've been such an inspiration for us,' and I'm like, 'What? Me? Get outta here!' "

"And this is your supervisor, right? The one we met?" Aileen clarified.

"Yeah, yeah."

"I told you I thought there was something wrong with him!" Patti said. Johnny ignored her.

"And has that problem in the township that you talked about before been resolved?"

"Well, there's really no problem, it's just-"

"He thinks he's going to get fired," Patti said. Johnny glared at her again. He didn't want to admit that he suspected something going on in Bart that would end badly for him; he certainly didn't suspect anything good going on.

Aileen saw the look he gave his wife and changed the subject. "And how about you? What's the latest with your health?"

He told them that since it was the halfway point in his treatment, they did another bone scan to compare to the first, and they'd know the results the next week. He also told them, with not a small amount of disappointment, that he didn't get a new PSA and didn't know why.

"I'm gonna feel real bad for the doc if the scan doesn't show much improvement because he's been so excited."

"I think Johnny's entertainment for them," Patti interjected after putting down her menu.

"How do you feel?" Frank asked.

"Oh, I feel great!" Johnny said as was his usual response. "I was telling the doc, though, for the past ten days I been feelin' this tingling in my chest like I did when I first started on the chemo. I'm hopin' it's just the Good Guys fightin' the Bad Guys again, like, maybe they found some more that came outta hiding and they have to take care of 'em, clean 'em up."

Before Frank could ask what his doctor said about that, the waitress arrived with their drinks and took their orders.

***

Before his fourth chemo session, the doctor gave him the results of the bone scan, a copy to take home, but no new PSA. Though the bone scan was good news, he couldn't help but wonder why they weren't giving him new numbers. Was there something wrong, and they didn't want to dampen his spirit?

He turned off the truck, parked in front of Hometown Builders' front door, and limped in.

"Well, speak of the Devil!" Dan said, springing up from his chair. Minutes earlier he had replied to an email from Audra and that had sparked a conversation about Johnny with his wife as she straightened up the office.

"Hey man!" Johnny said, dragging in at his regular volume, loud for anyone else. He shook Dan's hand and noticed Liz over the divider, whom he greeted in his sweet voice as he did all women.

They asked if he had gotten the results of the bone scan, and he reported his spin: all the tumors had disappeared, his doctor couldn't believe it, and it was all thanks to prayer and his attitude.

141

"I said, 'That's great, Doc! I'm going to celebrate by takin' some chemo and then play golf for a couple-a-days!' " Johnny laughed at himself. "He was like, 'Well, I've never had someone take chemo then play two days of golf!' " Johnny cackled while Dan grinned at him. "So that's what I'm doin'. After I finished eighteen holes this morning I came in here to see you guys!"

"I'm sure the medicine's been helpin', too, John." Dan said, getting up for some more coffee.

"Oh, no, no. He said that was part of it too, yeah,"

"When is that hearing for Gabriel? Isn't that comin' up?"

"Oh, don't remind me!" he said, and sat in a chair near the windows. He took off his visor to run his hand over his now completely bald head, sighing heavily.

"What's the matter, John?" Liz asked.

"Oh, it's just a big mess, that's all. I told you that I went over to Bill's house, didn't I?"

"This was a while ago?" Dan asked, walking back, coffee cup in hand.

"Yeah, like, a couple months ago when I first found out I had cancer, I went over to try to explain my reasoning for everything I did. I said, 'I did what I could to produce the biggest tax revenue for the township. I let him build two buildings where the one stood originally so he would be payin' more money in taxes,' but he didn't care. He still was screamin' that it was illegal, which it is not. And I said, 'Bill, if you think I've done something wrong, I'll resign today!' "

"John, you wouldn't really resign, would you?" Liz said, surprise in her voice.

"Well, if I wasn't wanted, sure!" (which was true in the moment). "And Bill was like, 'No, no no. We don't want you to resign,' then I'm like, 'So what's the problem?' "

"You can't resign, John. Who will keep us up on all the town gossip?" Dan teased.

"What are you talkin' about? This is where *I* come for the gossip," Johnny chuckled. 'This place is the biggest grapevine in Bart, second only to the Amish church!"

Abe came in from the back just in time to overhear the conversation. Johnny insisted that he didn't get paid enough to put up with that kind of aggravation. When he told them how much he got paid per month, no one could believe it was so little. Johnny was especially hurt because he had always felt like he had been doing the township a favor by taking so little money for the job.

"And on top of that, I'm goin' through chemo, Chester's not doin' well, and I'm afraid…" he said, wanting to say more but stopped himself.

"Do they know what's wrong with him yet?" Dan asked.

"Oh, I'm sure it's cancer, but the doctors won't confirm it," he said quickly. "And I really feel for him because the waiting is the hardest part."

"You know, Antique isn't doin' too good either. Have you been by there lately?" Dan asked.

"What? No!" Dan had the inspector's undivided attention.

"Yeah, he went to the hospital one night a few days ago. You didn't know?"

"No. Oh my gosh. What's wrong with him?" Johnny asked like his whole world was falling apart at once.

Dan thought he heard something about stomach ulcers, but he wasn't sure. Johnny wondered if it had to do with the pressures of being a bishop and having to shun his daughter who left the church. He knew it would give him ulcers if he had to shun one of his own children.

The inspector got up from the chair and staggered a little with his first step. "I better go over to see him," he said and passed through the restaurant side after Abe to order a sandwich and flirt with the waitresses. When he went to pay, the waitress told him it had been "paid for." This wasn't the first time it had happened. The other times the restaurant had been full, and he had assumed it was an anonymous customer. This time there was no one in the restaurant, being the middle of the afternoon, and his anonymous benefactor was obvious. Even to him.

143

Johnny at his 4th chemo session (photo by Patti Coldiron)

***

"Hey, man. You sellin' any antiques?" Johnny yelled from his driver side window as the bishop walked carefully down his concrete steps.

"Oh, no one wants to come on a day like this. It's too hot!"

"Listen. I was just over at the restaurant and it's been so stinkin' hot, I gave all the waitresses approval that they could all come in in their bathin' suits," Johnny teased.

Antique giggled and continued the joke, "Oh, well, that sounds like a good idea. You know, that's such a good idea, you tell 'em once they put em on, to stay on. Just enjoy the day."

Johnny laughed big.

"How are you doin'?" Antique asked before Johnny could ask the same about him. "Did you get the results of your bone scan?"

"Yeah, I got it. I'm great. All good news. I came here because I'm worried about you!" Johnny noticed he had come out to the truck slower than in the past. Ever since he had heard the news a while ago that Antique's daughter had left the church and he was shunning her, Johnny had wanted to somehow bring it up. He had even practiced his lecture a couple times: "Hey, bud. You brought her into this world. This shunning stuff don't fly with the Big Guy. The Big Guy is love. Plain and simple."

He never could find the right moment, and even now, assuming that stress was causing his friend's illness, all that would come out was a joke: "I heard you weren't feelin' too good and I was makin' sure you weren't worryin' yourself sick over me!"

The bishop laughed and told him he'd had stomach problems for years, but that he was feeling better now and appreciated him asking. When Antique asked details of the bone scan, he told him that all the tumors were almost gone, that the doctor said it all came down to prayer and a good attitude, and, Johnny was sure to add, that he'd had never known someone to play a couple days of golf after chemo but that's just what he was doing.

"Antique, I been meanin' to tell you su'um," Johnny said, "You got to tell your wife how much I appreciate her."

"Huh?" the bishop said, perplexed.

"I was over at... Oh, what's his name? Geez! This chemo brain!" Johnny took off his visor and rubbed his slick head with the clip-clop of horses hooves and the sound of a buggy in the background.

"The whole family left the church recently...," he said to himself trying to jog his memory. "They moved his wife's mother into a trailer with electric onto their place, and she's still Amish... Oh, Levi!" he said, shaking his head, disappointed in his brain.

"Well, anyway, his wife was tellin' me about how worried she was about the kids goin' into English school because she knew they'd be behind and your wife had been givin' them extra lessons." Johnny wasn't sure if the bishop knew that or not, but he wanted to

145

be certain he heard that the people he was supposed to be shunning were out there only saying good things about his wife, how nice she was, and how she helped them and the kids. "Antique. She's showing me that she has good Christian ethics, and I want you to go tell her."

"Well, John, you're right."

"That's why you call me The Roving Bishop!" he said, proudly. Just then, the inspector decided against the anti-shunning sermon he had rehearsed, and for a parable instead. "Oh, did I tell you who I saw when I went over to Mary's woodshop when they were rebuildin' it?"

"You mean the one that burned down a couple months ago?" Antique clarified.

"Yeah. Around the time I was diagnosed with cancer. And it was so weird because I had just been thinkin' about this kid who was into solar panels—he's not doing solar panels anymore—but I met him when he first started out when he called me up. I didn't realize he was Amish because he didn't sound Amish but he did have an Amish name. I said to him, I said, 'If you've got the blueprints for your solar panels,' I said, 'I'll come up and pick 'em up.' And he said, 'Oh yeah, I do,' he said, 'I'm on White Oak Road.' And I said, 'OK, tell me where on White Oak,' and he explained it and I was inspecting his parents' house! I was like, 'Wait a second!' I said, 'You're Amish!' He goes, 'Yeah.'

"So I drive straight there and walk in, and here's this young boy, didn't speak with an accent, had tremendous plans, and a computer there was spittin' 'em all out. He starts explaining inverters and all the different things for solar panels and everything, and, you know me, Antique, I'm just a dumb hillbilly, so I understood nothing. I finally looked at him and I said, 'Boy,' I said, 'You didn't learn all this stuff at Amish school.' He started laughin' and he went in the back and brought out his certificates for all his extra schooling for solar. Just a very, very interesting boy.

"Well, I hadn't seen him in, probably, two or three years. I think the last time I saw him, he was goin' somewhere on one of those scooters. So there I am at the woodshop with everybody helpin' to rebuild, and all of the sudden I look over, and there's Ira in English clothes! I had known that his parents were having a hard time keepin' him in the Church. And there he was working there and he has English clothes on, and I go over and I shake his hand and I said, 'Ira! How you doin', man?' He said he's now an electrician out in York county workin' as an electrical contractor.

"So I got the chance to talk to his sister, Mary, and I said, 'Mary, what's Mom think about this?'—meaning Ira being English now—and she said, 'Well, Mom's a little upset but,' she says, 'John, let me tell you something. Ira's one of the nicest people that God ever made, and he's my brother, and the Church is not going to make me shun him. He will always be my brother, and I love him very much, and Mom sees it the same way.' And I said, 'Well, sounds like we're finally making progress in the Amish church!' " Johnny laughed loudly and waited for the bishop's response.

Antique just sighed and changed the subject. "You know, Mrs. Fisher is not doin' well. She had her fourth chemo session, too, and they've said she can't take anymore."

***

After completing his second round of golf in two days post chemo treatment number four (just like he told his doctor he was going to do), Johnny lifted his clubs into the bed of his truck and drove away to Georgetown. With the tallest corn he'd ever seen on either side of the road making the twists and turns along the way extra dangerous, he listened to his messages, crossed off "Hartefeld," and added three more names.

He pulled into the gravel parking lot and forced himself to bound into the Bart Township building, as much as his arthritic knee would allow. "Give me some good news, Grace!"

"Well, we go to the oncologist on Tuesday," she said, trying hard to sound positive. "He's so tired, John."

"Oh, I can relate!" the inspector said with a heavy sigh, thinking how much more tired he was after his two days of golfing than he thought he'd be, but wanting to keep up the appearance of

147

strength and hope for Grace and Chester. "I tell ya, though, my doctor said a lot of my success can be traced back to my good attitude, and I told him, I said, 'My good attitude comes straight from all the people around me,' like you, Grace!"

"Oh, c'mon, John," she said, not wanting to take any credit for his improvement.

"It's true!" he squealed. "Now, of course, my daughter Audra has been my personal angel through all this. Maybe you should talk to her."

"Oh, we have been talkin'."

Though he thought it odd, he didn't ask questions. "Well, I think you should talk to her some more!"

Later, while riding around Georgetown from inspection to inspection, he wondered why Audra would be in contact with Grace. He called her to get the scoop and to give her the update. She explained that she had been talking to Grace about the book. She was also very interested in Chester's sudden diagnosis, but he didn't think that was unusual.

***

Johnny arrived home more tired than he could remember ever being and just wanted to rest. He couldn't believe two days of golf made him feel so drained and started to suspect the chemo had something to do with it. He thought about Mrs. Fisher and Chester and now worried about Antique, figuring it was worse than he was letting on. He thought about himself, too. All he wanted to do was sit in the recliner and sleep.

Patti heard him come home and shuffled out of her bedroom where she was trying to make sense of the tiny print on the bone scan report that the doctor had given them.

"Have you read this, Johnny?" she asked, holding the report.

"No," he said, turning on the TV and nestling into his recliner.

"Well, I think you should."

"I don't want to. I want to rest for a minute."

148

"Well, I think you should know what it says," she insisted, her brow creased in it's permanent position. "It's your body!"

"I already know what it says, Patti."

"You do? How do you know?" she asked, calling his bluff.

"The doctor told us what it says."

"Johnny," she cried, standing over him with the papers in her hands as he laid in the chair with his eyes closed trying to ignore her and everything else he felt. "The doctor didn't tell you about the tumors in your lungs that have grown since treatment started!"

Her words felt like a brick on his chest, sinking his hopes. She was right. The doctor never mentioned that. He opened his eyes and involuntarily snatched the papers out of her hands.

"Where does it say that?" he snarled. She pointed to the place, but he couldn't read it anyway though his eyes were better than before the cataract surgery a few years ago. His head spun and everything swirled inside of him. He tried to stay cool but could feel his temperature rising. "What do you think they will do about it?" he asked calmly with a scowl though he really wanted to scream.

"I don't know," she said, desperation in her voice.

He shoved the papers toward her. "I just want to get a nap, Patti."

"Why don't you want to know about this?" she cried, taking the report back.

"I don't want to talk about it!" he barked. "I'm tired. I been workin' my backside off!"

"You were out playing golf with your men friends!" she jealously corrected.

"I was out workin' before you ever got out of bed, Patti. All you do is sit around and do nothin' all day!" he screamed, nearly making her ears bleed. "I'm the only one who ever does anything around here, and I'm the one on chemo!"

"Knock it off, Johnny!" she shouted back in a huff. Instead of continuing the match with her feelings hurt like she always had, this time she tried something new: she walked back to her room, leaving him alone in the recliner like he wanted.

He closed his eyes. *What if things take a turn for the worse?*

he thought, then demanded his chemo brain to stop. He didn't want to think about it anymore. He was tired of worrying, tired of keeping up appearances, and tired of wondering about the future. He made his mind focus on the drone of the sportscaster and before long it lulled him to sleep.

Johnny in his recliner in front of the sports network

CHAPTER 17

Late July

On the next Wednesday appointment, Dr. Caruso wasn't there, much to his patient's disappointment. Johnny looked forward to his weekly check-up to kid with the young doctor almost as much as to hear his treatment progress.

While a nurse took his vitals, he told her about golfing for two days after his chemo session a week earlier and how completely exhausted he still was because of it. She asked him if he wore sunblock to which he replied, "Does it look like I wear sunblock?" pointing to his leathery head as proof that he didn't. She suggested he start since the sun saps your energy and using the lotion would help. She also suggested instead of slathering on Coppertone, he could wear a hat that covered the top of his head. She drew some blood and sent him on his way to Bart.

After crossing off a few names from his list, he stopped by to see Grace. He knew she and Chester had the appointment with the oncologist the day before and steeled himself for news of the worst as he walked through the door to the township building's office.

"I better hear some good news from you, Grace!" he shouted in his comically happy voice from the back of the narrow room by the water cooler.

She dropped what she was doing and swiveled her chair toward him. "Oh, John, we don't have any news. It's so frustrating!"

she said, close to tears. "Since the biopsy stated 'very suspicious' instead of a positive for cancer, the oncologist can't really do anything until it is confirmed. He couldn't even order a PET scan because the insurance company won't pay for it."

"What? I thought it was confirmed to be cancer!"

"Well, it's like the oncologist said when we were in there: 'If it walks like a duck and looks like a duck,'" she quoted then chuckled, "and then Chester said, 'then it's a goose!'"

Johnny laughed a dramatic belly laugh that filled the small office.

"They did prescribe some pain medication for his uncomfortable pain spells, though. Chester's supposed to be here any minute and we're goin' to an appointment with the surgeon. Although if the oncologist couldn't do anything until it is confirmed, I'm sure the surgeon can't either. It's all just a mess!"

"Oh, God. Waiting is the hardest part. I only had to wait days for my treatment to start, and, man, that was hard enough." Waiting for the hearing was killing him, too. "I can't imagine waiting weeks!" Just then, Chester walked through the door.

"Chester. Man. Listen, you gotta stick with me. You gotta stick with me. I'm goin' with ya to your next oncology meeting and I'll get you hooked up to somethin', even if it's the exhaust pipe to the car!"

Grace and Chester laughed and appreciated their friend's exuberance.

"We have to be patient," Chester said. "We'll go one day at a time and whatever the Lord has in store for us, we'll accept as graciously as we can."

"I guess that's all we can do," Johnny said though he didn't want to believe it. He thought there must be something *he* could do. "Well, good luck, man. I was just checkin' in. Now I'm goin' golfin' with Huston and the boys!"

***

152

His buddies had invited him to free golf again, and, on the way to the course, he stopped by a Walmart to buy some sunblock and a hat to replace his visor. When he met up with Huston and Ronnie at the practice green they were surprised to see him rubbing the cream on his head, face, and arms. He explained the nurse told him it would help him not get so tired in the sun.

"I thought you were doin' a pretty good impression of Frankie," Huston said, referencing their pale friend who obsessively applied the stuff in all seasons.

"Did you finally turn Amish?" Ronnie asked, pointing to his straw hat.

"Not unless the Amish get their hats at Walmart!" he joked as Paul Hess walked up on the green to round out their foursome.

"Paul!" Johnny exclaimed. "I didn't know you were the other guy today!" Paul worked for Wawa's corporate office, and Johnny hadn't seen him since Mose had offered the finder's fee if he could get a Wawa convenience store built on his ground. They shook hands, and Paul asked how he was feeling. He told him he was "great!"

"Oh, I'm tellin' ya, the difference in how I'm feelin' now compared with what I was feelin' two months ago? It's like night and day, it really is. I tell ya, I didn't know how sick I was." As they walked to the first green and spun the tee to see who would go first, he told Paul about the golfing trip where he caught pneumonia and the boys made him promise to go to the doctor.

Johnny didn't want to come right out and ask Paul if he knew anyone he could talk to about getting a Wawa built for Mose. That would be awkward. Maybe if he told a couple Amish stories he could go into Mose's rock-n-roll story, then casually bring up the Wawa. If he could make the Wawa a reality, he could buy a house. He wouldn't have to live right under his son and get annoyed when he sat inside all weekend or didn't wake up before 9:00 am.

He had heard rumors that the little, yellow vinyl-sided house at the edge of their development, catty-corner from his old farmhouse, might come up for sale soon. Living there would be ideal. He'd still be close enough to Brooke's kids and Young John's kids so that they could all walk over regularly and raid his junk food paradise; Patti could still see the barn.

Not only would that house be practical, but it held sentimental value for him as well. His dad, J.R., had it built some thirty-five years ago for, incidentally, an Amish couple whom he had hired to work the farm the old-fashioned way like he remembered from his youth in the mountains of North Carolina. Before the couple moved in, their bishop came to inspect the house and insisted that the electric be removed. Never one to be told what to do, J.R. fired the couple before they ever started, put them up in a trailer on the farm until they found new employment, and sold the house.

"Oh, boys, did I tell you the one about the privacy fence?" Johnny asked. It didn't sound familiar to Huston or Ronnie. "One time I got a call from this one Amish guy on 896. I helped him put what's called a 'Granny Flat' in behind the house. Well, they have a double house and him and the wife moved into the Granny Flat. He called me up and said, 'John, I think I might need a permit.' I said, 'OK, I'll be right on down.' I get down there, and I said, 'Ben, what is it you're wanting?' He goes, 'Do I need a permit for a privacy fence?' I said, 'A privacy fence? Where?' He says, 'I want to put a privacy fence up between my Granny Flat and the house.' I said, 'How high?' 'Eight feet.' 'Ben, yeah, you need a permit, but why?' 'John, we don't need lessons.' I told him, I said, 'Ben, you're looking at this whole thing wrong,' I said, 'This is what you do, bud,' I said, 'You and the wife get in front of your windows then you charge them more money for rent and for the bedroom lessons that you're also throwing in!' He thought a minute and he goes, 'John, that's why we love you. You always have a different viewpoint!' His audience laughed as he made his shot.

By the 10th hole he had gone through the stories about the fire trucks going around the bishop, the man who owned the grocery store whose family was dispersed, the kids who ran from the school because they heard an angel tell them to, the Amish electrician, the kids on scooters with cell phones, flirting with the ninety-one-year-old lady, the U-Haul with the clothes, Ira and the solar panels, being invited to preach in the Amish church, and finally he got to Mose,

154

the former rock-n-roller in a wheelchair.

"So, Mose, he bought this ground a while ago and when he did he said, 'John, if you get a Wawa there, I'll make it worth your while.' " Johnny didn't want to mention the exact amount he was offered. That would sound crass.

"Oh, that's cool," Paul said. "You know what? Let me give you a name to call about that." He looked through his phone and texted Johnny the contact. "The guy's also a member of this golf course."

"Hey, thanks man!" the inspector said, thrilled to have a lead. For the rest of the eighteen holes the conversation varied from things his doctor said, things he said to his doctor, old golf stories, and few more Amish ones. By the end, he had lost all his money, but he did have a name that might be worth a lot more than what he could fit in his wallet.

***

Johnny raced back to Bart to cross some names off the list before calling it a day. As if he wore blinders like the horses that trotted by, he didn't notice the tasseling corn or the men and boys in straw hats and suspenders that drove the teams of horses in the fields, harvesting the first of it. His mind was elsewhere, more specifically on Chester and on Gabriel's hearing the next day. Every now and then he allowed himself to daydream about actually getting the Wawa for Mose. If that happened, he could buy the little, yellow house and Patti would be happy that they owned their own home again. It would be wonderful.

As he was almost out of Bart on his way back to his basement apartment, his phone rang. He glanced down for a split second to answer it, narrowly missing a buggy that seemed to appear out of nowhere.

It was Audra calling for the latest update.

"I tell ya, I was so used to the nurses hovering over me like mother hens that now in these past few times they haven't been like that, I..." he said with disappointment as he searched for the right words, "I just don't know what to think. When I go, and they don't give me a new number, and I don't even see my doctor, it's kind of... it's... I don't know, not as much fun, I guess."

Audra asked when he'd get a new number.

"Oh," he said with a little more umph, "they said I'll get a new number next week and I'll know. It will say to me whether it's still workin' or not."

They chatted a little while longer when the subject of his dreaded hearing came up. "I just have a feeling it's going to be bad," he admitted with a heavy sigh.

"What do you mean? Bad for you?" his daughter asked, surprise in her voice.

"Yeah, maybe. We'll see." The wheels in his head were spinning as fast as the chemo would allow.

"You don't think you'll actually get fired because of this, do you?"

"I don't know, but if they start to go in that direction, they're gonna get a little surprise," he said mysteriously, remembering what Aileen had told him a while ago.

***

For a week now he'd been talking about the upcoming hearing to anyone who would listen. Abe thought he overheard Bill say Johnny's name at the restaurant one day, and it spun the inspector's imagination into overdrive. Johnny was sure Bill was furious now and whipping up support to oust him. He told Frank and Huston and their wives the tale at dinner when they went out to eat at the local golf course's restaurant on Saturday for Franks' birthday.

The scenario got worse and worse the more he thought about it. At one point he had almost convinced himself to preemptively resign, though there would be no decision that night regarding anything and his position wasn't even in question.

He spun the saga at his inspection stops around Bart and to anyone else who would listen at the Hometown Kitchen where he'd stop for lunch. Johnny was afraid they'd "get rid of him" and would

156

paint the possible future scenario in different ways until the bearded, suspender-sporting man listening would say a variation of "they'd better not!" Although the Amish didn't vote, it made him feel good to have so many people on his side.

Thursday afternoon he pulled up to Young John's house and noticed for the first time the tractor in the middle of the horse pasture that had been there for a few weeks. He walked down the brick pathway, let out his dogs, and rested up in his recliner in front of ESPN for the 7:00 pm hearing in Bart.

Young John walked downstairs to his father's living room. "Hey Dad. What should we do about the tractor?"

"What tractor?" he asked, playing dumb.

"The tractor we bought."

"I didn't buy a tractor," Johnny said, specifically remembering that he told his son he didn't have the money for one.

Young John explained that the Amishman he "bought" it from kept calling asking for the money, but he'd decided that he didn't want it after all. It was too small.

"I have a suggestion," Johnny said, irritated. "Go talk to the guy and tell him the tractor is too small, and you'd be happy to pay rent for the time it has been at the farm."

When Young John returned upstairs, Johnny closed his eyes and let out a big, exasperated sigh, bothered about the hearing and the fact that his son didn't even come down to ask about it, or how he's feeling. It seemed like his son only talked to him when he needed something. He sulked nervously thinking about the confrontation that was coming next and almost talked himself into not going at all. His sense of duty and responsibility got the best of him and at 6:30 pm, he started up his truck and sped to Bart.

CHAPTER 18

Early August

The township building's small office space was packed. Aside from the three supervisors, Larry, Bill, and Chester, also present were two lawyers, the three hearing board members who would decide the case, Grace, Gabriel and his attorney, Mose, Jake, the man who actually poured the concrete, various other involved community members, and Johnny. Although the place was standing room only, it wasn't as big of a turn-out as he had expected. There would have been no need to move it to the fire hall as he had thought.

The session began with one of the attorneys reading the reason for calling the hearing. Later, all Johnny could remember was his supervisor screaming at him.

"That building is illegal! You can't have an accessory structure. It says so right here in article 103!" Bill shouted, pointing to the passage out of the code book he held. "You can't have this. It's an accessory structure and the roof's too high!"

"Bill," Johnny said calmly, doing his best to keep his cool despite feeling tricked, "it's not an accessory structure. Read article 807. Article 807 states you can have two principal uses on one lot."

"You cannot!"

"Bill, yes, you can, and you're the one who told me—you and Larry—you both told me I could handle it however I wanted if I could get Gabe to tear down the old building, and I did."

"But what you did is illegal!"

"No it wasn't, Bill. What *you* did was illegal!'

Suddenly at a loss for words, Bill stopped dead. A confused look crossed his face. The clip-clop-jangle of a passing buggy could be heard through the silence.

"Remember the day I stopped in here and you, Larry, and Chester were here going over road costs or something? And I said, 'Gabriel's buying ground, and I know it's gonna be a problem, so what would you like done on the property?'"

Bill nodded and folded his arms.

"And you said, 'Oh, well, we want that intersection improved. We want him out of the right of way. We want him to tear the old building down.' And Larry agreed, and you go, 'Building down. That's what we would like. After you get that building down we don't care what you do with it.' Didn't you?"

"Yes," he said coldly.

"Now, Chester over there," he said, gesturing dramatically to the man who leaned against the wall with his wife, "he never said a word." Then, leaning forward with the one eyed squint he used when he really wanted to shock and surprise, he asked this: "Do you want to know why Chester never said a word?"

Bill drilled holes through him with his eyes, his face as sour as spoiled milk, but said nothing.

"The reason Chester didn't say a word was... it's illegal!" Bill looked at him like he had just spoken Pennsylvania Dutch. "Three supervisors can't be together and make a decision unless it is a public forum—and it *wasn't* a public forum!" Johnny sat back and crossed his arms triumphantly. He looked at the board for a reaction. It wasn't the shock and awe that he had expected, so he continued:

"Look, you gave me the directive, and I did it. I got it torn down. To get Gabriel to tear it down I told him he could have two buildings, which is what he wanted." He looked at the hearing board. "Everything I did was in the best interest of the community. I told him we had to control the stormwater, the runoff on the lot. He did that. I told him he needed another exit on the lot so the traffic could be a better pattern. He did that, too. He did everything I asked him to do," Johnny explained and turned again to Bill. "It wasn't until the

159

second building went up—the one that is closer to your house—that you ever had a problem with any of it, and with two buildings he pays more taxes!"

Bill, like a stubborn mule, stood firm insisting that the second building was illegal and that it should be torn down. Johnny started feeling a tingle in his chest. After minutes more of heated discussion, he felt a stabbing pain, distracting him. Before long the head of the board said they'd heard enough; their decision—whether Mr. Glick would have to tear down the building or not—would be announced in three weeks. For Johnny that meant three more weeks of worry. Three more weeks with his position in the community and, he believed, his life hanging in the balance.

On the way out Johnny passed by the man who had actually poured concrete at 4:00 am that sparked Bill's ire. "See what your early morning pour cost me?" he said bitterly, and limped out to his truck without looking anyone in the eye. He grumbled to himself that only the Amish appreciated him and these English didn't and never would. He was the only one trying to help the community. He was the one who understood that in order to save the farms you had to help the farmers. The English obviously didn't get that the only people who were farmers in the community anymore were the Amish. Without him, they'd have a tough time with the English becoming more and more resentful due to their prosperity when the rest of the country suffered through a recession.

On the drive home, the tingling in his chest and head intensified. He had the horrible feeling that his days left as zoning officer of Bart were numbered but hoped it wasn't the end. He hoped the decision would be in Gabriel's favor and that Chester would recover. Most of all, he hoped his work wasn't done.

***

The next morning like usual, he got up at the crack of dawn, let out his two dogs to run around the yard, and noticed the grass. It was getting high. He *needed* to mow; he needed to mow not just for the lawn, but for his own well-being. On the mower he could give his

160

brain a break and only think about cutting the grass and following the lines. He vowed to get to it that afternoon and daydreamed about mowing golf courses for a living. He looked to the field where Young John had abandoned the tractor after attempting to cut the weeds in the pasture with the under-powered machine and shook his head with a sigh. After returning the dogs inside, he wrote out his to-do list for the day:

8/7
———————————
GRACE
HOMETOWN
JOHN RICHARD
DAVID KING
JOHN SMUCKER
JAKE GLICK
JAKE BEILER
AMOS ESH
AMOS FISHER

He stood at the bottom of his brick pathway, now alive with purple coneflowers, and gazed to the top as if it were Mount Everest. His diminished strength and weakened balance made each wobbly step harder than the last, so climbing to the top and getting to his truck without stumbling had almost become an accomplishment worth noting.

If the cancer didn't kill him, he mused on the way up, the chemo just might. He had come to think of the cancer-fighting intravenous drug not as a friend, but an enemy of an enemy, a necessary evil. It took all the hair on his body and sucked up all his moisture, leaving his tanned skin dry and thin like paper. Lately he felt as if he had been beaten by a 2x4, his whole body tired with a deep soreness all the way down to his core. His golf game was dreadful. It was claiming him, little by little, but he was determined to hold on.

He tried hard to keep his spirits up, but the contention over the Nickel Mines project didn't help. Based on how twisted up and red Bill's face had become during his tirade the night before, Johnny

161

was sure now he would do anything in his power to remove him. He needed to be in Bart in the perpetual prayer service; it had created a miracle.

Yes, Chester had promised nothing would happen to him as long as he had anything to do with it, but now even Chester wasn't a sure thing. He needed to be there for Chester. He needed to be Chester's cheerleader. He couldn't lose Chester. Chester was becoming the key to his whole existence, and the more he thought about it, the more hopeless and dire the situation became.

***

In Georgetown he trudged into the township building office without his usual sparkle and greeted Grace. She noticed his lackluster shine and knew what was bothering him without having to ask.

"Do you have anything for me?" he said as down as she'd ever seen him.

She said she didn't.

"I guess this is one of the last times I'll have to ask you," he said with a sigh.

"What are you talkin' about, John?" she said sharply, knowing exactly what he meant.

"Last night was bad," he said, shaking his head and looking down at his loafers.

"Oh, John. I didn't think it was that bad," she said, trying her best to reassure him. "You know, after you left last night Bill comes up to me and Chester and he says, 'I bet John's gonna be mad at me now!' I told him, I says, 'No, Bill. John Coldiron doesn't get mad.'"

Johnny chuckled sadly, but her comment made him feel a little better. He liked the person she saw him as and wished he could be him all the time.

"Now, don't you worry about it anymore. You've heard what Chester has said, right? Anyway, you have bigger fish to fry."

He nodded but didn't want to say that he was afraid that her husband wouldn't make it.

"I tell ya, Grace, I don't get paid enough to take this kind of bull. You know all those checks you've written out to Municipal Solutions? I've never gotten any of them. They all go straight to Young John." Though it was true, he didn't mention it paid the rent, in love with the idea of martyrdom.

Grace shook her head in disbelief, but the mention of the inspector's son reminded her of a conversation she had with him not too long ago. When the subject of Gabriel and the hearing had come up, Young John joked that maybe his father should stay away from Gabriels since an Amishman by the same name had beaten him up when he had first started in the inspection business. Unbelievably she'd never heard that story. She wanted to get the scoop but not as much as she wanted to get her co-worker's mind off his troubles.

"Speaking of your son, he was telling me the other day about another Gabriel who beat you up. What was that all about?"

Johnny could hardly believe that he had never told this one. It was one of his first stories and still one of his favorites.

Immediately his mood lifted, and he became the Amishland Storyteller. "So there was this one fellow in East Nottingham, an Amish guy who was burning plastics, and the neighbors were complaining about the fumes so I get a call to go over. I get there and as I pick up a sample to take with me, he saw me and rushed over. So I said to him, I said, 'Gabriel, you can't burn this stuff, it's toxic!' He said, 'Give it to me!' I said, 'No, I'm keeping it as a sample of what you're doing!' He tried to grab it away from me and I wouldn't let go, and he twisted the thing and got me off balance and fell on top of me. Well, when he fell on top of me, the plastic cut me right below the eye and I started bleeding down my face."

"Goodness!" Grace said with a smile, eyes wide.

"So I got up and called the state police on my cell phone right then to turn him in for burning the plastic. When they show up, there I was with blood running down my face standing next to an Amishman. I can only imagine what they thought!" Johnny paused to chuckle. "The officer asked me what happened and asked me if I wanted to press charges, and, of course, I didn't, I just wanted him straightened out.

"Well, by the next day the Amish guy's calling me because

he had gotten a hold of his bishop and the bishop had told him he better straighten it out, that it was his problem. So then, by that time, I was working more here in the Bart township area doing building inspections, and I was doing inspections for this Amish shed builder down the road. He asked me where I lived, and I told him. He said, 'Oh, I've got problems down there. My son-in-law beat up the building inspector down there!' I was like, 'I know. That was me!'" Johnny chuckled and sighed. "He became very apologetic and after that, the legend of Johnny Coldiron grew. I became a little famous around here after that." His face brightened as he chuckled more. Grace's ploy worked.

As he limped out the door, his phone rang. It was Audra wanting to know how the hearing went. He told her what he remembered: it wasn't good.

"I need a break from all this, and I really want to come down to see you," he said. "I was thinking that my last chemo session will be on September 2nd, so I'll be free to go places after that, and that weekend is Labor Day Weekend, so that would be perfect."

"Uh," Audra stammered, "you don't want to come that weekend…"

"Why not?"

"Uh… Traffic. Everybody wants to come down here to the beach, and the traffic will be awful. You know how frustrated you get when you are stuck in it!"

"Oh, I don't care about traffic," he insisted.

"Uh… well…" she stammered again but he didn't notice. "OK, Dad. I'm coming Wednesday for your next appointment so we'll talk about it then."

***

After dropping by Hometown Builders to reenact the hearing for Dan, Liz, and Marvin, and to remind them that they needed to get a move-on with their rental house project, Johnny drove over to Mose's office to drop off a blueprint. The wheelchaired architect was meeting with another Amishman about a project, and when Mose

164

spotted the building inspector entering the office, he called him over to introduce his client.

"John, this is Elmer." They shook hands as Mose explained to his client that the English man standing before them was a building inspector who might be able to help with his project.

"Elmer is trying to put an Amish Market up in West Chester in an old Acme store," Mose said, and pointed to the blueprints. Johnny took a quick look and asked to take them home so he could go over them more closely and maybe even get his son involved. He then went on to tell the men all about the hearing, how he was sick of all the politics, and how he just wished he could mow grass for a living.

"Now, I gotta study this a little bit," Johnny said to Elmer. "Give me your phone number, and don't do anything 'til I talk to you. That's the deal here. You gotta listen to me." He looked at Elmer with a serious glance, bringing his thinning eyebrows closer together. Elmer looked at Mose, not sure how to take the man.

"Oh, geez!" Johnny said in his big, joking voice. "You don't know!"

Elmer still looked confused.

The architect shook his head. "Oh boy," he sighed and playfully rolled his eyes to the drop-ceiling. "Here it comes."

Johnny explained. 'Yeah. I... I'm a little different."

"Oh, that's for certain!" Mose retorted with the start of a grin.

"Here in Bart I'm also the zoning officer and, uh, let's put it this way:" Johnny said mysteriously, "do you know Antique, the bishop?"

Elmer said he did.

"Well, Antique calls me 'The Roving Bishop,' " Johnny announced. "So the deal is, you gotta do what I say."

Elmer promised he would and, after saying goodbye, the inspector tossed the plans behind the seat of his truck and sped around the lush rolling hills. As he dashed here and there, picking up checks and collecting information for permit forms, teams of horses pulled wagons down the roads carting crates filled with the first apples of the season that Amish girls and boys had gathered.

He thought about how much he liked these people he worked with everyday and how he would feel like he somehow let them down—and let God down—if he were removed from his zoning officer position there in the township. He started to think maybe God was done with him after all, like Antique had suggested, and that's why all this was happening: the hearing, his illness, Chester's illness. *I'm not done,* he swore to himself. *On Wednesday we'll know.*

At his next chemo session Dr. Caruso promised to give him his new number. He was nervous. The new tingling in his lungs worried him. What if the new PSA was still 3,000? Or higher? He wasn't ready to go.

In the early afternoon he went back over to the Hometown Kitchen for something to eat and to chat but was surprised he was the only customer there. After ordering the special like he always did without looking, he took out the blueprint and spread it on the table. Immediately he saw a catch and called Mose who returned his call in short order.

"Hey listen. On the print very plainly, it says that they're holding him to a 75-foot egress pattern," he said, "but it also says right on the plan that this old Acme building has a sprinkler system. As soon as you have a sprinkler system, the egress pattern goes up to 250ft, so he doesn't have an issue if it has a sprinkler system, and it says it on the plans!"

"Oh my goodness. You know what?" the draftsman said. "You don't need to mow grass. You need to be a consultant."

Consultant. Yeah. I could be a consultant, he thought. The idea appealed to him since he had basically been doing that all along. If he worked as an official consultant, he could charge for it, knowing the Amish would be happy to pay for the service. Many times when he would pick up and deliver the forms and permits they'd ask him how he got paid, concerned that he wasn't making enough money.

After finishing off his cheeseburger, he went up to pay. "You're meal's been taken care of," the waitress said with a friendly smile. He insisted on paying, but she wouldn't let him. "Now John," she said as if she were disciplining a child, "you have to be a good receiver."

But a good receiver he was not.

166

Johnny mowing his backyard

Johnny and Frank in golf cart, mid-80's (photo courtesy of Dave Huston)

CHAPTER 19
August 12, Penn Medical Center

Johnny punched the elevator button to the second floor of the Kennett Square branch of the Penn Medical Center and smiled at his wife and oldest daughter at his side. He was nervous. Those tingling sensations in his chest concerned him. So did the part of the bone scan that Patti pointed out that said a few of the tumors in his lungs remained and had enlarged. If he didn't hear good news on this visit, he didn't know how much longer he could hold out hope with worry occupying more and more of his exhausted chemo brain. He worried about Chester, his position as zoning officer, and how, and if he lost it, would he make money in the future... and if he even had a future at all. Today he would know. The door slid open and the threesome stepped in the elevator.

"Hey Mr. C. How are ya today?" Paula said as they entered the waiting room, like she hadn't seen him in years.

"I'm great!" Johnny said, conjuring sparkle while his wife and daughter took seats behind him. "I get my new numbers today."

He wrote his name down on the sign-in sheet as she stared at her computer's monitor in front of her, clicking away at her mouse.

"Mr. C, did ya hear about that fire in Parkesburg?"

"No!" Johnny said with much more enthusiasm than warranted. He took the closest seat to the receptionist and crossed his arms over his belly. "My son is actually the zoning officer up in Parkesburg."

"Oh, well, there was a house there that burned to the ground. Apparently the people who lived there were hoarders. Do you ever watch that show, *Hoarders*? I can't watch it. All that stuff makes me feel claustrophobic. I've got to throw things away. Sometimes my husband will want to keep something, like a plastic bag, and when he's not looking I'll throw it away."

"I've got an Amish family in Strasburg, and the wife is a hoarder. The same thing happened to them—their house burned down, but not all the way to the ground."

"It's a disease!"

Johnny agreed.

Just then Dr. Caruso walked through the entrance, carrying his laptop like a briefcase, crossed the waiting room between Paula and his patient, and uttered a quick "Good morning" before disappearing again through the door to the offices, taking Johnny's attention with him. Paula continued:

"I can't believe there are Amish hoarders. I didn't think Amish people really had stuff, you know? Sometimes I'll go up to the outlets in Reading and I'll see the buggies and the women with those little hat things on. What are they called?"

"Huh?" Johnny asked, his thoughts on what the doctor would tell him in less than an hour. He needed good news.

"What are those things called the Amish ladies wear on their heads?"

"Bonnets?"

"Yeah, and they'll be driving those buggies with, like, fifteen kids crammed inside, staring at you out the back with their big eyes when you pass. Those little boys with the straw hats are just so adorable. I wish I could buy a little Amish boy doll."

Johnny had nothing to say since he had only been half listening over his own deafening thoughts. The office door opened and a tall nurse in scrubs appeared holding a clipboard. "Coldiron?"

"That's me!" Johnny said, and slowly stood erect so his balance could catch up with what his legs wanted to do.

"Good luck today!" Paula said as the family walked through the doorway and into the hall.

***

Johnny sat on the papered, cushioned table in the corner, his palms sweating as Patti and Audra took the only two chairs in the room, aside from the roller stool that the doctor would occupy in a few minutes. A nurse took his vitals: weight: 229, blood pressure: 139 over 91.

"About the same as last time," Johnny remarked, reassuring himself as the nurse left. He looked to his wife. "Huston has a question he wanted me to ask."

"I want to ask about the bone scan and the tumors that are still growing," Patti said with concern as deep as the vertical line between her neat eyebrows.

Long seconds of worry hung in the air. What would the doctor say? Would the patient be part of the unlucky 50% with his condition who die within a year of diagnosis? Would they go home today and begin planning for his funeral? Or would they find out his work wasn't done and go home today high on a cloud? What news would he be spreading around Amishland later that afternoon? Johnny looked at his hairless shin swinging above the floor. A quick knock at the door interrupted the silence, and in walked the doctor.

"Good morning everyone." He set his laptop on the counter, opened it up so it would boot, and sat on the roller stool. He turned to his patient. "How are you feeling?"

"I'm feeling great!" Johnny insisted. Only if he were at death's door would he answer otherwise, and maybe not even then.

"Good," Dr. Caruso said and drew in a deep breath. "I saw your PSA last week and it was…"

Johnny's heart momentarily fluttered in the micro moment that his doctor paused to find the right word. There was no clue in the young man's face. Was it good? Bad? Horrible?

"Fantastic," the doctor finished, slightly more animated than usual, almost smiling.

Johnny felt a wave of relief washing over him. He exhaled dramatically, letting go of all the tension and worry he had built up in the past couple of months that went without a new count.

"I think I remember the number," the doctor said folding his arms over his chest, "but I want to tell you the exact number, so I'm waiting for the computer to boot." He looked over at his computer that was still starting up with "17 out of 20" on the whirling screen with blinking dots underneath. "Seventeen always takes the longest."

"Well, I wanted to ask you about the tumors in his lungs that are still growing," Patti said like *her* life depended on it.

"What tumors that are still growing?" the doctor asked as if he had no idea what she was talking about.

Johnny smiled at his wife in a mix of nervousness, relief, and a little "I-told-you-so," suspecting she had been blowing things out of proportion all along.

"It was in the bone scan report," Patti said, now unsure of her answer.

"Huh. I don't remember that," Dr. Caruso said but without his computer and all the information on it, he couldn't say for sure. "It was probably just within the margin of error." He explained how tiny the things measured on the screen are, so a millimeter off might result in a misleading reading.

They were all relieved to hear it, but Johnny most of all. "So, Doc," he started, smiling now, "a golfing buddy of mine wanted me to ask you somethin'."

"OK," the young medical professional said, anxiously stealing glances at his computer's progress.

"So, compared to the first time you saw me and now," he paused wondering if the doc would guess his question, "would you say my chances are better?"

Dr. Caruso's eyes lit up and he nodded several times. "By a lot. Not by a small margin, by...," he paused, searching for the right word again, "by light years."

"That's what I wanted to hear!" Johnny cried in his big, happy-fun voice and lifted both arms above his head like a football referee calling a touchdown. "I tell ya. I'm excited to get chemo!"

The doctor chuckled. "We need to get you a new hobby!" Patti and Audra chuckled too, but Johnny threw back his head and let out an enormous belly laugh. While Johnny's laugh eventually devolved into a sigh, the doctor leaned back on the wall behind him, crossed his arms again, and kept one eye on his computer's progress.

"So," Johnny started, "after this last chemo session in three weeks, what happens next?"

Doctor Caruso explained that after the last chemo session, he'd get another bone scan and continue on the Lupron. Every three months blood would be drawn with a new PSA. Besides that, nothing would be done unless the PSA starts rising, or new symptoms appear such as a new pain, or eating or sleeping becomes uncomfortable again.

"I tell ya, I feel like I been real fortunate. I go see this Amish lady every week or so who was diagnosed around the same time as me," he told the doctor who was only half listening to the story, distracted by the progress the computer wasn't making in starting up. "I mean, she's hooked up to oxygen twenty-four-seven and, like, I almost feel guilty. They look at me and say, 'You don't even look sick!'"

"You have done very, very well. You'll be amazed with your new number," the doctor said, tantalizing his patient. "You know what? Someone has a desktop down the hall. I'll see if I can get the number from that." He stood up and hurried out the door.

In less than a minute the doctor returned with bad news: "The internet is down!"

Johnny felt like the wait might just kill him. The doctor sat back down on his stool and crossed his arms again. "At times like these, you long for the days of paper charts. Not that I was around then..."

Johnny filled the time by launching into a golfing story. "You know how the Lupron lowers your testosterone?" the patient asked, not pausing for an answer. "Well, the other day I was out golfin' with my buddies, and they say, 'You're not going on you're own?' See, we usually play in pairs, but you're required to go on your own at least once in a round or you have to pay in $5 at the end. And I said,

'I can't!' They were like, 'Why not?' I go, 'You know I don't have testosterone!' " Johnny cackled and slapped his knee while Dr. Caruso laughed politely, still distracted by his computer.

"Yeah. Sports Illustrated did a story on the games we play." That piqued the doctor's interest, causing his brows to raise slightly. "We got this one guy—he's a dentist—Stevie Niemoeller, but we call him Captain Nemo. He's the guy doin' all my dental work. He's got, like, four houses all along the east coast, and he complains about the dollar bets being too much money!" Johnny cackled again but spared his arthritic knee this time. "So... so when we play with him we have to bet fifty cents. We call those Nemo dollars!"

The doctor checked on his computer's progress again and sighed: "I feel so powerless!"

An awkward lull ensued that Johnny felt responsible to fill. "Well, now, every time I've gotten a new number it's gone down by, like, 60%, right? First it was 22,000, then 9,000, then the last time it was 3,000. So..."

The doctor's eyes lit up again. "Oh. It's *much* better than that," he said with more inflection than usual.

Patti gasped. Her eyes brightened.

"Yeah," he confirmed, nodding seriously with his eyebrows lifted and looked to the three faces eagerly staring back at him, filled with hope. "Like, think about taking off a zero."

"Really? Wow!" Johnny shouted, clapping his hands. "That's like the time it came down to 9,000 from 22,000 and I was like, 'That's pretty good, huh?' And you were like, 'That's not good—that's great!' Oh, shoot!" Johnny chuckled and sighed with a smile. "Life is about stories. You know, when ya go through a problem like this, you learn about what really matters in life."

Johnny almost launched into another story when the computer finally booted. "It's up!" Doctor Caruso exclaimed and quickly pressed a few keys to retrieve the actual PSA count. Johnny leaned forward on his hands. Audra held their breath. Patti's mind went blank. Finally, after a few seconds that seemed like hours, the long awaited information was revealed and Dr. Caruso looked to the three faces again.

173

"How does 118 sound?"

Gasps and cheers of "Wow!" and "That's amazing!" could be heard all around.

"Oh man!" Johnny started in his loud, joking voice. "You're gonna be talkin' about me for a long time, aren't ya?"

Dr. Caruso agreed wholeheartedly, cracking a bit of a smile with an emphatic nod.

"Hey, Doc. I got a little bone to pick with ya," Johnny said in a deadpan, attempting to tease. "On that bone scan report, it says I'm 'grossly unremarkable.' Now, what are you tryin' to say?"

The younger man, without expression, began to explain the benign meaning of the medical phrase.

"I knooow! I'm just kiddin' with ya!" Johnny said, cackling.

The doctor went on to describe which specific treatments would stop and which would start in three weeks. "Now, the cancer *will* someday grow again," he said, looking around the room to the three joyous faces smiling back at him. "However, assuming nothing else comes up, I do expect that even after the chemo stops, your PSA will continue to drop. I'm not sure what the biggest driver is, but I suspect the Lupron."

"Which one is the Lupron?" Patti asked.

"It's the shot he gets in his tushie—the one that lowers his testosterone. But," he continued and addressed only his patient perched in the middle of the room, "you are doing beautifully, beautifully, well." Then the doctor, cracking an almost imperceptible smile, said, "You're grossly unremarkable."

***

The family left on a cloud, thanking the doctor on the way out. They filed into the chemo dispensing room, identical to the ones in the other locations with the same vinyl chairs filled with the same sallow and bone-weary patients, and took their seats. One nurse came over to turn on the machine and dispense a bag of sodium chlorine to flush whatever might have been in the line previously. Meanwhile, Johnny, smiling the entire time, clumsily texted his buddy, Huston, who had asked him to report the news in that manner as soon as he knew something.

"Hey, Audra, what was the word the doctor used when I asked him what Huston wanted to know?" She had taken notes the entire time.

"He said…" She paused to scan through a couple pages and found the exact phrase. 'Light years.' "

"Light years. I love it!" He finished his text and in a few minutes when the bag was empty, a different nurse arrived to hook up the chemo to the patient's port. Patti took a picture.

Johnny leaned back in the armchair and started going over things he had to do that day that included attending an Amish birthday party. "Oh—I was in the township building talkin' to Grace yesterday and she was tellin' me how Chester was doin' and said she's havin' a surprise party for him on the 5th, so…" he paused and looked straight ahead past his daughter to deliver what he thought was bad news. "So I've got to go to that. And, of course, that was the weekend I wanted to come see you."

"Oh, don't worry about it, Dad," Audra said with a wave, suppressing a smile. She and Patti grinned at each other when he wasn't looking.

Just then, the doctor crossed the room to the nurse's station and, with uncharacteristic excitement in his voice, asked the women if they'd seen Johnny Coldiron's latest PSA.

"Hey!" Johnny shouted from his chair by the wall, pointing at his doctor. "I told ya you'd be talkin' about me!" The nurses giggled which was always his goal.

When the hour ended, Johnny checked out and they all exited to the hallway. Patti pressed the elevator button. As the door slid open, Johnny, in a now-rare spurt of energy, raced down the stairs as fast as his knee would carry him.

"I always beat her to the lobby," he said to his daughter behind him with a twinkle in his eye. "She hates it!"

175

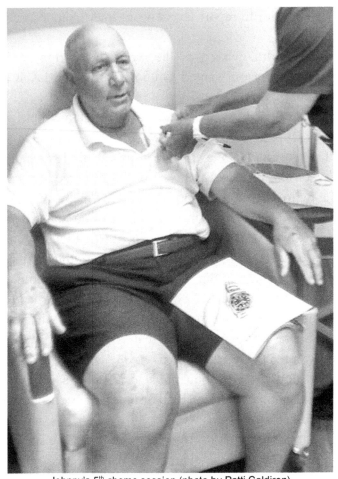

Johnny's 5th chemo session (photo by Patti Coldiron)

CHAPTER 20

August 12, Amishland

"Light Years! I love it!" Johnny repeated with a happy sigh and crammed himself back into his cluttered truck. He looked down at his list and crossed the first one off.

8/12
~~LANDENBERG BILL~~
LEON'S PARTY
JAKE BEILER
JAKE KING
JAKE STOLTZFUS
JAKE KING BELL RD.
MOSE
AMOS

"OK. We got that one done!" he announced and paused. "Man. I was going to say something. Chemo brain. I tell ya…"

"The consultant idea?" Audra reminded him about what he had been talking about before the first stop.

"Oh yeah," he said and steered toward Amishland. "So Mose —the draftsman—said after I figured out this one thing that was gonna save his client a lot of money, he goes, 'You don't need to mow grass, John. You need to be a consultant.' " He chuckled with a proud smile.

"You don't need to mow grass? What does that mean?"

"Well, I told him—and I told your mother the same thing—

177

my dream job is just to mow grass on a golf course. I wouldn't have to deal with all the politics," he sighed and rolled his eyes the best he could while still keeping one of them on the road. "So, anyway, I told your brother when we were going over the blueprint, I said, 'John,' I said, 'you're actually more certified and qualified than me.' He actually, in that township around West Chester, he used to be the building inspector."

"You mean my brother, John?" Audra asked, her eyebrows raised.

"Yeah. So I said, 'John. Do you wanna go up there and meet the guy that wrote these comments and talk to him about the prints?' I said, 'You can sit down and point out these couple-a things. Everything could just go away, everything be approved. I guarantee I can get them to pay you two or three thousand dollars to do that.' I said, 'Do you want to collect it?' And he never would say 'yes'!"

"Seriously? I can't get answers out of him either!"

"No! You can't get answers out of him. And I'm like, 'Don't you want the money?' Aah! He drives me crazy. He... he, uh... What was it he did just the other day that drove me nuts?" he asked himself, squinting in an attempt to make his brain work better while navigating a windy, back road on the way to Bart.

"Oh!" he said and told her the story about the tractor. "So, the next thing I know he calls me up and he goes, 'Abner said that his brother was going to buy the tractor and the same thing happened to him. He said it was too small!' " Johnny sighed, shaking his head.

Turning left on the sunny mid-summer afternoon, they passed an apple orchard with boys and men all wearing straw hats and suspenders, collecting the fruit and placing them in giant, cubed, wooden containers, but Johnny didn't notice.

"It's just... like... he depends on me, but then on the other hand, he doesn't talk to me at all," Johnny said, wishing he had the kind of relationship with his own son that he had had with his father, whom he looked up to more than any professional baseball player ever.

Before long, he slowed to a stop in front of a building along the road in the midst of a renovation, and put the truck in park. "Here

178

we are. This is the Amish birthday party you wanted to go to."

"Who's it for? Anyone I've met?"

"It's for Leon Stoltzfus. He's the fiberglass guy."

"Is he related to Dan Stoltzfus?"

"It's his brother."

"Oh! Do you think Dan will be there?" Audra asked with a little too much enthusiasm.

"Probably!" he said without wondering why she sounded so eager to see him.

They got out of the truck, entered the gutted building with concrete floors, and passed a skid steer where a couple English construction workers sat eating plates of food. Johnny said hello to them as he and Audra walked on by to the center of the party where twenty or so Amish people of all ages gathered around a pile of 2x4's where the food was being served buffet style: meatballs, rolls, coleslaw, and chips. Johnny stood to the side of the line as people greeted him.

"This is my daughter, Audra," he announced.

"Oh, yes! We've met before," Dan Stoltzfus said and secretly winked at her. He reminded his wife, who stood in line next to him, that she was the one writing Johnny's book.

"Oh! Nice to meet you," Liz said. "Are you the youngest?"

"No, I'm the oldest. I just look like the youngest," Audra said with a sly grin inducing some chuckles. Johnny introduced her to Abe and his wife, Catherine, as well as the guest of honor, Leon, and his wife.

"She's riding around with me today. She came for my chemo appointment this morning."

"How did that go?" Liz asked.

"Oh, just fine," he said and uncharacteristically didn't launch into his latest amazing story.

"Dad!" Audra exclaimed and looked at him as if he just blew her mind. "Aren't you going to tell them the story?" It wasn't like him to pass up being the center of attention. He jumped at the invitation, pretending to do so begrudgingly, and retold the story of the dramatic drop in PSA, ending with his favorite part:

"And then I'm sittin' there takin' the chemo, and here comes my doctor talkin' to the nurses. He says, he goes, 'Did you see Johnny Coldiron's PSA?' I yelled from across the room, 'See? I told ya, you'd be talkin' about me!' " Johnny laughed big as the crowd laughed, too, and expressed their happiness at the news.

"So, keep prayin'. It's workin'!"

Johnny mingled with the mostly young, hatless and beardless Amishmen who were leaning against the bare cement wall, holding plates and looking hot and uncomfortable on the steamy August day with sweaty faces and their long-sleeved shirts rolled up to their elbows. He retold his latest troubles with the township and what went on at the hearing to anyone who would listen, collecting opinions and quotes in his favor.

Meanwhile, Audra stayed on the other side of the room with the women and struck up a conversation with Liz, Catherine, and Leon's wife who were sitting on a pile of lumber eating their lunch. While Johnny stood at the center of another group of Amishmen telling them the story of the hearing, he noticed Dan and Audra talking. He thought it was nice that they were being friendly with one another.

Audra took pictures of her father there at the party with his friends. Once back in the truck, she asked him if the Amish were still weird about having their picture taken. It had long been rumored that the Amish didn't allow photos of themselves, considering them graven images.

"Nah," Johnny said confidently, though he just assumed.

"Are you sure?" she asked. "I felt like all the men were staring at me."

"Oh, they were staring at you," he chuckled, "but not because you were takin' pictures." He looked at his list. "Now. Where to next?"

***

As they made their way down the road through Amishland with their windows down, the smell of fresh-cut hay wafted in the air. Whole families in uniform—mother, father, and their ten children—could be seen cutting alfalfa and tobacco plants one by one to dry in the sun on the hot and muggy mid-summer day.

Johnny made a left turn into a driveway. "Wow. C'mon. This will be... C'mon!" he said to his chemo brain, trying to remember the name of the man he'd known for years and goes around telling stories about. "The musician..."

"Mose?"

"Mose! Gosh. How did I forget that? Now, but in his other life he was who?"

"Tom Petty?" she said with a shrug.

"Tom Petty or... or... Rolling Stones..."

"Mick Jagger?"

"Mick Jagger! Oh my God, it's Mick Jagger! Ya gotta remember that. You gotta razz him a little bit about Mick Jagger," he said with a grin, putting his truck in park behind Mose's family business garage that housed enormous road construction vehicles.

Audra shook her head and laughed at her father as she opened the door to get out. "You love to razz!"

"You betcha. That's part of my job!"

He managed to get out and stood still for a moment to catch his balance before moving forward toward the open garage door and through to the office. The blueprint he came to pick up lay on the table in the middle of the small room surrounded with computer and blueprint machines.

"Mose isn't here!" he said and looked side to side as if he might have somehow missed him. "Maybe he's at the house. I'll call him." Stepping outside with his back to the house, he dialed his number, put his phone to his ear for a few rings, then announced that there was no answer. "Gosh, I was hoping you could meet him."

"Dad, I met him before, remember? When you were first diagnosed and I rode around with you?"

"Oh! That's right." Johnny put his phone away and turned to the truck when he saw Mose rolling himself around the corner in his high-tech wheelchair.

"There he is!" he said to his daughter, pointing. "Hey!"

181

Johnny shouted across the paved parking lot. "There's Mick Jagger!" As he got closer he introduced his daughter again to the man and told him she had wanted to see Mick Jagger. Audra tried to imagine him playing and singing "Free Falling" or "Satisfaction," and couldn't do it.

"How are you feeling?" he asked.

"I just had chemo this morning, my PSA is now down to 118 —that's from over 22,000, and my daughter's riding around with me. How could I not be feelin' great?"

"Glad to hear it," Mose said then turned to Audra. "Good to see you again." Audra smiled and said the same.

"Hey man," Johnny said, shaking the rolled papers in his hand, "I've got the blueprints and I'll let you know."

They chit-chatted a while longer, then as Johnny walked back to the truck, he mentioned, almost as a side note though it had been on his mind the whole time, "I'm still workin' on that Wawa. I've got a lead!"

"Sounds good," Mose said simply, giving away nothing.

"OK. We're outta here. I'll keep you posted!" As the inspector and his daughter shut the doors of the vehicle and came to the end of Mose's driveway, Johnny stuck his arm out the open window and pointed. "See those three houses along the road here?" Three two-story, white buildings in a row stood at the edge of the property, one quite large with stone pedestals that held the porch columns. "He wants to tear them down and build new. You wanna know why?"

"Why?"

"Because he thinks they're ugly. Now, don't tell me he doesn't have money!" The inspector put on his left turn signal and darted out before an oncoming buggy. "I don't know if he remembers this, but he told me once that if I could get a Wawa on his property, he'd give me a big finder's fee, and let's just put it this way: I could buy a house."

"Oh, really?" Audra said, almost unable to believe it. "So… are you working on that?"

"Yeah, well, Paul Hess, one of my golfing buddies who

works for Wawa, just the other day said, he said, 'John. Let me help you out. You need to talk to this guy.' I can't remember his name right now, but I got his name and number in my phone. I don't know why he gave it to me."

"Were you telling him about trying to get a Wawa for Mose?"

"Yeah."

"Well, obviously, he was trying to hook you up. C'mon, Dad! What other reason would he have for doing that?" She looked at him with an amused and slightly incredulous expression.

"I don't know. We'll see," he sighed with a dreamy smile and continued to the next stop on the list.

***

The pair motored around the countryside from inspection to inspection and stopped at one farm, parking between a carriage and a skid steer. Heat radiated from the dark pavement as Johnny, with Audra in tow, marched up onto the back porch where the family was just finishing up lunch. Behind them on a line from the porch to the nearby garage hung many pairs of black trousers in various sizes with names stitched on them with white thread.

Johnny introduced everyone. Audra said she remembered meeting them a couple years ago when she had ridden around Amishland with her father for the first time. The stout, grandmotherly woman with beautiful, friendly blue eyes wearing a plain, green dress and black apron had a stately air about her. Her husband, sporting sideburns and a long beard, sat across the table from his wife. Children of all ages entered and exited the porch as a young woman in a plain, blue dress and black apron came through the screen door from the house to clean up all the plates.

"Audra, this is where the girls had class after the shooting until the new school could be built," Johnny said, pointing to the three bay garage.

"Oh!" she said as a connection was made from name to face. "You're Amos and Elsie King!"

"Yes," Amos answered, twisting his head around as far as it

would go to the right while sitting back in the faux-wicker, plastic white chair.

"You know, Audra is writing a book about me and all my experiences with the Amish," Johnny said proudly, gesturing toward his daughter.

Elsie reminded him that he had told them about that at the party they hosted a couple months ago. "There's another book coming out about the Happening by the gunman's mother. It's coming out in a couple months. It's called… Oh, what is it called? There's one by his wife called *One Light Still Shines*, and the one by his mother is…"

"*Reflections*," the young woman finished as she wiped down the table.

Elsie added, "We see her every year when we go by to carol in front of her house, but she's not doing too good."

Johnny sat in the rocking chair in the corner and mentioned his chemo session that morning and the encouraging doctor's appointment. Audra pushed him to retell the story, and again, he jumped at the invitation. There on the porch he described the doctor's visit that morning from start to finish, with the King family hanging on his every word.

"How amazing!" Elsie said when he finished.

"Well, I told the doc, I said, 'I got a lot of people prayin' for me!'"

"Yes, you do!" she said. "Yes, you do!"

"And he even said that was even better than what he could do," Johnny paraphrased.

Amos asked Johnny for his opinion on an addition to his garage, so he left Audra on the porch with the women. The Amishman showed his friend the space where the addition would go, and inspector gave him his best advice. They walked back through the middle bay of the large garage, past a set of golf clubs and a young man who was busy banging out horseshoes, eventually settling into Amos' small, cluttered garage office.

They sat down in the room's two available chairs crowded by filing cabinets and stacks of paper spilling over the desks, the walls heavily decorated with murals, turkey fans, and antlers. There, Johnny went on to tell Amos his latest trouble with the township while his bearded friend listened intently with his arms folded across his blue short-sleeved shirt, vest, and suspenders.

"I've just got a feelin' that Bill's so mad he's gonna gang up with Larry and get rid o' me!"

"Oh no, he won't. They don't know what kinda trouble they'll have if they do that."

"I just need someone in there I can trust... And I've known you probably as long as I've known anyone around here," Johnny said, warming up to the topic he really wanted to discuss.

"Yes, I remember inviting you to a devotional on opening day for the new school. It really hurt me that you didn't come."

"I know, man. I know. That's one of my biggest regrets. I was just tellin' Audra that a few months ago."

"Well, John, you trust Chester, don't you?"

"Yeah, but Amos, I'm tellin' ya," Johnny sighed and shook his head, "I don't think Chester's gonna make it much longer. He's really, really sick. I mean... it's bad."

"Oh, I didn't know he was so sick. I'm sorry to hear that."

"Amos, I tell ya, I'm gonna need some help in the township, and you Amish won't even vote, let alone run for office!"

"Well, John, you never know what might happen."

Johnny on the porch spinning his tale from the morning

185

Johnny spinning another tale in the garage office

***

This vague comment got the inspector's wheels spinning on overdrive and plunged him deep in thought as he and his daughter drove down the road to their next stop.

"You know," he said to his passenger, "Amos was on the township's planning board when he was much younger. I think I might be able to convince him to fill the supervisor spot if... if something happened to Chester. I was there with him and Elsie one time, I said, 'Listen. You Amish need to protect your way of life or it will be taken away,' and Elsie said, she said, 'Amos. John speaks the truth!' " He chuckled, sighed, and after a brief pause added, "Used to be the Amish women would never speak up but, boy, they do now!" He chuckled again.

"Hey," he said, changing the subject, "let's go by and see Grace." Turning down the road toward their destination, they passed a buggy with a scooter strapped to the top. "I almost feel bad about telling her my good news with Chester as bad as he is."

As they approached the Township building, Johnny became concerned when he didn't see Grace's car parked in front. "Uh oh," he said, furrowing his brow. "That's not good."

"Is she usually there this time in the day?"

"Yeah. Gosh, I hope nothing's happened with Chester," he said, imagining the worst.

***

On the way back home with the tape recorder rolling, he retold two of his favorite golf stories, both featuring some variation of gastrointestinal distress, occasionally laughed so hard he nearly ran off the road. A mile from his basement apartment, he turned onto Fulton Road and stepped on the gas, accelerating much too fast for the short road lined with cornfields that featured a ninety degree bend in the middle.

"Man, I've really got to go to the bathroom," he said, leaning closer to the steering wheel and speeding up.

"Why don't you just pull over?" Audra suggested, gripping the passenger door.

"Yeah, that might be what I have to do!" Right before the curve he slammed on his brakes, skidded into the neighbor's driveway, and disappeared into the cornfield. Many, many minutes later he emerged, stomping out between the stalks with a scowl on his face. "Here. You drive," he barked at his daughter and threw her the keys.

"What's the matter?"

He sighed heavily. "I shit myself," he grumbled and climbed into the bed of the truck. There he rode all the way home with an embarrassed frown, deeply disappointed in his body. No longer could he claim that the chemo wasn't making him sick and found no humor in the situation. However, if it had happened on a golf course, it would have been hilarious.

187

Johnny inspecting pre-fab Amish construction, August 2015

Playing cards after dinner with friends, August 2015
Dave Huston, Cheryl Huston (eyes only), Patti Coldiron, Aileen Parrish, Frank Parrish,
Johnny Coldiron

CHAPTER 21

Mid August

Monday morning Johnny got in his truck and zoomed toward his favorite place on earth that wasn't a golf course, winding through the hillsides, lush with green as far as the eye could see. He knew Chester was to have his surgery that day and worried about it almost like his own mother worried about him. His phone rang and he answered it.

"John?" a shaky voice said.

"Grace?" he asked, not recognizing her cell phone number, having never had it in the nearly nine years they had worked together. "Are you at the hospital?"

"Yes, and we've been here since yesterday. Oh, John, he got real bad yesterday, and we had to rush him here ahead of schedule."

"Oh my God!" Forgetting anything else he had to do that day, he slammed on his brakes, preparing to turn around. "Are you at U of Penn?"

"Yeah."

"I'm on my way!"

In less time than it usually took, he arrived at the University of Penn hospital in Philadelphia and navigated to the room where Chester lay with Grace and her two sisters sitting beside his bed.

"Hey, buddy!" Johnny boomed in his big, happy voice as he shuffled into the room, hoping to lift Chester's spirits. "How are you feelin'?"

"Not too good, John, not too good," Chester said weakly. "They drained two liters of fluid outta me yesterday. It's hard to eat or drink anything because I already feel so full."

Johnny wished he could do something. When he asked what he could do, Grace suggested he tell one of his stories to get Chester's mind off his pain and requested the U-Haul story. Wanting to be helpful, he happily obliged. If nothing else, he figured it could lighten the mood.

"OK. You want the U-Haul story? You got it!" He laughed a little, shuffled back and forth, adjusted his straw hat, and shoved his hands into his pockets. "Me and the boys were headed down to Mountain City, Tennessee—where all my relatives are from—to play golf. We got to Roanoke, Virginia, and the rear end went out in my Suburban, and we didn't know what to do. So, it was late at night, about ten or eleven o'clock, and there was a place across the street that was a U-Haul center. So we went across the street to talk to 'em and they didn't have anything for us except a big box van so we took it." He paused to look around and add to the mystique.

"So here we were with a big box van, three golfers in the front seat, five in the back with all the golf clubs, and all closed up. Now, we still had two, two and a half hours to get to Mountain City up these windy mountain roads, even windier than the ones in Lancaster, but with a steep drop-off on one side. So, we get to Mountain City, and once we got there, everybody who was ridin' in the back was not feelin' too good because you got some fumes and the roads that kind of loop back and forth. The next day we head to the golf course in the mountains, where you feel like you are actually teeing off into the clouds, you are so high. We had one boy, this one boy jumps out of the back and says, 'Before I ride back there again, I will go and buy a car. I'm not ridin' back there!'

"Well, we figured out a method. We went back to the unit that we were staying in, we got the sofa out of the unit and put it in the back of the U-haul, and then everybody fought to get in the back of the U-haul because we had the cooler. We had everything sittin' back there. It was our own livin' room. It was awesome! Now, you gotta realize, when you pull up to a fancy restaurant and roll up the

190

back and all these guys jump out, people are gonna start to wonder what's going on," he paused to chuckle at the scene from years ago playing in his mind.

"But the best part of the U-haul was, we were drivin' to the golf course the next day—and the roads are so narrow that nobody can pass because you risk goin' over the mountain—and there was this pickup truck behind us, really close because he's wantin' to pass. Huston's in the back with me and he looks and he goes, 'Oh, man. Look at these guys in this truck. They can't get by and they don't look happy. And they've got guns, too!'—they had a rack with guns in the back—and Huston goes, 'They've got Skoal hats on. These guys are gonna get mad and they're gonna shoot us!' He says, 'I know it! They're gonna shoot us!' " Johnny paused to breathe and chuckle.

"Well, the truck kep' tryin' to get around the U-haul, but they couldn't get around. Finally he got just enough room to get around and he *floored* the truck. And as he goes around the U-haul, the truck backfires. Huston dives over the couch and onto the floor to protect himself because he was sure that *they were shootin' at him*!"

Everyone in the room, including Chester, laughed big.

"You just can't make this stuff up!" Johnny exclaimed nearly in tears, still cracking himself up. "I tell Grace that all the time. And I got a million of 'em!"

Grace talked her co-worker into telling her favorite one about the time he tried to pick up a golf game with some guys he recognized, but didn't realize he had forgotten his clubs. He happily recited that story, too. Before Johnny left the room to return to Bart, Chester, with a sly grin, asked the man he had been responsible for hiring if he'd do him a favor.

"Anything, man. You name it!"

"I want you to kick Bill's ass for me, will ya?"

Johnny laughed heartily at the fight the older man still displayed in what he feared were his last days. He assured him he'd be more than glad to.

"I love you, man," Johnny said to his boss and friend lying on the bed hooked up to multiple machines that were humming away, sustaining him.

"Right back at ya."

191

Johnny Coldiron, Dave Huston, Andy Jennison, John Conner
Rebecca Hostetter tournament at Moccasin Run Golf Course in Atglen, PA, 2016
(photo courtesy of Dave Huston)

***

Johnny pulled up to Hometown Builders to see Dan and tell him all about Chester. When he walked in, he was disappointed when only Abe was there in the construction side to pick something up.

"Hey Abe!" Johnny yelled. "Is Dan around?"

"No, Dan hurt himself on vacation. He won't be in for a few days."

Before Johnny could ask for details, the phone rang and Abe walked over to the caller ID out of curiosity. "Ha. It's your daughter. What are the chances of that?"

"My daughter? Audra? Why would she be calling here?" he said totally confused and squinting hard.

Abe shrugged.

Johnny made a mental note to call her and reminded Abe that

they need to get on their restaurant expansion project if they want to get the lot done before the pavers shut down for the winter. Abe sighed and explained how it kept slipping their minds due to their workloads.

"You act like you got chemo brain!" Johnny joked as he said goodbye and limped out the door to his truck, pausing for a couple breaths. Everything was getting harder now. Undeniably, the chemo was taking a toll, but it wasn't going to let it take him down. He pulled his phone from his pocket and dialed Audra, curious about the call.

"Hey Dad! What's up?"

"Did... did you just call Hometown Builders?" he asked, climbing into his cab, confused and almost certain Abe had been wrong.

"Uh... what?" He didn't notice the surprise in her voice.

He rephrased his question. "Did you just call Dan Stoltzfus? Or... Abe?"

She paused, her heart beating wildly. "Yeah."

Now he was really confused and had to know. "What's *that* all about?"

"Oh...," she paused again and stammered, "uh... I was just calling to see if I could interview Dan, you know, for the book."

"Oh. OK!" he said, starting up his truck, chuckling. "Because I was just over there and the phone rang and Abe looked over and said, 'Oh, it's Audra' and so I had to call to see what was up. I was like, 'What's Audra doin' callin' Hometown Builders?' " he said and chuckled again. "All's good!"

"How's Chester?" she asked quickly, changing the subject. "Didn't he have an appointment at the hospital today?"

"Grace actually rushed him there yesterday. Oh, he's not good. Not good at all," he sighed. "You know, Grace has that party for him on the 5th, and... and I don't even know if he's gonna make it 'til then."

"Oh no. Really?" Audra said with too much interest, though Johnny didn't notice that either.

Wednesday morning at 8:00 am, Johnny drove to his weekly appointment for his blood work. He only saw Dr. Caruso in passing in the hallway as he hurried to his next patient. Johnny told him all about Chester's sudden and intense battle with pancreatic cancer, to which the doctor said that, though there was always hope, it sounded like little could be done. He also proudly relayed Brooke's phone call from a couple days ago when she told him what a doctor customer of hers had said about his starting PSA number:

"She said, 'I hate to tell you this, but there is no reason your dad should still be alive!' " the patient chuckled.

Dr. Caruso found no humor in it. "Unless she is *your* doctor, she is *not* qualified to give you any sort of prognosis," he said authoritatively and without expression. "What do I always ask you when I see you?"

"You ask me how I feel."

"Right. That is what is most important," he said, nodding sharply in punctuation. "Like I have said since the beginning, the number doesn't really mean much. It's how you feel, and if we can stop the cancer from growing—which we have."

On the way from Kennett Square to the University of Penn hospital to see Chester again, he thought about what his doctor said. He did feel good—at least better than before the treatments began—but he was growing weaker with each chemo session. However, unlike Mrs. Fisher who had stopped after her fourth session and experienced a dramatic decline, he was determined to get through them all. However, the effects were cumulative. If the last one had driven him into the cornfield, what would this final one do to him? The ringing phone on the dashboard interrupted his thoughts.

"It was OK," he told Audra who wanted to know how his appointment went. "I just saw my doctor for, like, a second in the hallway, and I told him about Chester, then I told him about what Brooke's customer said, and I tell ya! He got all worked up and nearly jumped down my throat. I mean, he really got mad. He said, he goes, 'She has no right to be tellin' you that! She knows nothing about you!' He goes—and he's all worked up—he goes, 'What is the first thing I ask you every time I see you, huh?' I said, 'You ask me how I'm feelin'.' He says, 'That's right. And don't you forget it. That's what's important!' I'm tellin' ya, I'd never seen him like that. It was almost scary!"

"That's weird that he got so upset."

"Yeah, I know! And when I told him about Chester's condition, he just shook his head and said that there's almost no hope. I feel almost guilty that I'm still here. I mean, I was the one who was supposed to die. Not Chester."

"How is Chester, anyway? Anything new?"

"He's not good. Not good at all. I'm… uh… I'm on my way there right now," he said, distracted with a million disjointed thoughts.

"Oh, yeah?" she said, distracted, too. "Oh, Dad, I forgot to tell you…." But she hadn't forgotten; it was one of the reasons she had called, to set up plan B.

"Yeah?"

"I got an invitation from my friend, Jenn—you know, whose baby has your same birthday?

"Oh, yeah, yeah."

"Well, she's having a party for her on the 5th because they are going to Disney World the next weekend, so I figured I'll come for that and while I'm there we can celebrate your end of chemo and an early birthday."

"That sounds wonderful! We'll all go out with Huston and Cheryl and Frank and Aileen. That will be fun and give me something to look forward to!"

"Perfect!" she said, because it was. It was exactly what she wanted him to say.

"Well, after I see Chester I'll call you with the update."

***

Once in the hospital room Johnny was shocked to see the man who, just two days ago, had some fight left in him. The nearly lifeless

195

figure in the bed looked almost nothing like the same person. His paper-thin eyelids covered his blue eyes and the inspector was unsure if his boss was asleep, just resting… or worse. He grabbed his toe poking out of the sheet and said, "Hey. I love ya, man."

Though weak and nearly inaudible, Chester managed to return the sentiment one more time. Johnny stood for another moment reflecting on his own illness and how unfair it was that he should live and Chester should die. He was the one that had been so eaten up with cancer that no one could believe the count. Chester's cancer hadn't even been confirmed until Sunday when he came in for emergency treatment. Johnny stepped out into the hallway with Grace where he gave her a big hug. They both wept. He asked for her cell number so he could check up on her.

On his way to Amishland his thoughts were racing even faster than his truck. Chester was dying. How long before he was next? Someone would be appointed to supervisor in Chester's place, but who? If it were one of Bill's friends, he'd be voted out for sure, then he might really be next. What if he could convince an Amishman? There had never been an Amish supervisor, but there needed to be with the township being mostly Amish. It would make history. He was pretty sure he was already making medical history, so why not try? He drove straight to Amos's house to test his luck.

***

Johnny told Amos the desperate situation and got his friend to at least agree to think about accepting the nomination if it came to it. Johnny stopped by Dan Stoltzfus's office to share the news about Chester. He was surprised to see his friend hobbling along to refill his coffee.

"What have you done to yourself now?" he asked, momentarily forgetting everything else.

"We were up in the mountains, and I needed to cut a branch off this one tree. So, I got the ladder and I propped it up on the branch, and-"

"Wait. Don't tell me I almost got Liz!" Johnny said, inserting a callback.

Dan gave a sheepish grin and continued, "I propped it up on the branch and started sawin' away at it, then all the sudden the branch gives way and my ladder falls-"

"And let me guess—because that was the branch it was leanin' against?"

Dan nodded and groaned.

Johnny shook his head and laughed so loud Dan nearly had to cover his ears. "You mean to tell me *you* are 'Amish stupid'? *You? You're* almost English!"

Dan groaned louder.

"How hurt are ya? Have you been to a doctor?" Johnny asked, all jokes aside.

Dan told him his doctor said he had a fractured vertebrae and to rest in bed for a few days, the reason he had been out all week.

"I don't know if you heard, but Chester's in the hospital and, man, I don't think he's gonna last much longer. I saw him on Monday and the difference from then to now is unbelievable."

"Oh, no, I didn't know that. That's too bad, John."

"Yeah," Johnny continued, "and Grace has this surprise birthday party for him on the 5th… and there's no way he's gonna make it that long." He shook his head sadly. "I know they're gonna get rid of me when Chester's gone, but maybe they won't if the right supervisor is appointed… like an Amishman. I don't think there's ever been an Amish supervisor. It would, like, make history!"

"I'll do it!" Dan said almost jumping up, forgetting his injury. He winced and put a hand on his back.

"I wish you could, man, but you don't live in this township."

"Oh, well, my business does," he said. "That should count!"

"I think I have Amos King talked into takin' it if I can somehow get him nominated."

This surprised Dan. Amish didn't vote let alone run for office. Johnny explained that he wouldn't have to run because, when a supervisor dies or leaves his or her position, a temporary supervisor is appointed. If the right person were in there, he could turn the tide in his favor until Bill calmed down. "Yeah. I just need

197

to think some more and this stupid chemo brain is in my way!"

"Well, John, you'll have your work cut out for ya, that's for sure," Dan said and took a sip of coffee. "Hey, what are you doin' next Tuesday?"

"I don't know, why?"

"Can you take my place in the golf tournament? I was supposed to play on that day."

"A golf tournament?"

"Yah."

"With other Amish or Amish-lite?"

"Amish-lite?"

"You know, Mennonite."

Dan chuckled. "It's with Abe and a couple of other guys, but I don't know who they are. Abe set it up. Why?"

"Well, this one time a long time ago, I went on a weekend golfing trip with some Mennonites, and they were just terrible. This one guy hit his ball in the water, and another guy said, 'What a lovely splash,'" Johnny said in a mockingly pseudo-feminine voice. "I was like, 'Are you kidding me?' They were too nice! I couldn't take it. I took my clubs and drove home. It was the only time I quit in the middle of a round!"

Dan just laughed and took another sip of coffee. Johnny left, and having mentioned Chester's birthday party, he unknowingly reminded Dan to reply to Audra's emails.

CHAPTER 22

Late August

Early the next morning as Johnny poured the first cup of coffee of the day, his phone rang. Somehow he could tell by the ring it wasn't good news, and he dreaded answering it. For half a second he considered letting it roll to voicemail so he could pretend a little while longer that Chester wasn't dying. He stared at the phone in his hand, walked outside for reception in the early dawn, and answered. It was Grace. She was on her way home from the hospital. Chester was gone.

He felt hollow. Suddenly his good spirit that everyone, including his doctor, credited with his incredible recovery, had instantly vanished, as if Chester took it with him. He let his dogs loose to run around, then let his mind loose to wander, gazing past the shadow the house cast, and into the future. He felt bad for Grace. She was going to have a tough time without Chester. Heck, *he* was going to have a tough time without Chester. Without Chester, he was a goner. Soon Bill would oust him and he'd be without the community whose prayers had been responsible for his miraculous recovery—or so he believed. But why would God reverse his malady only to forget about him now? Surely he wouldn't, but sometimes Johnny couldn't understand the things God did. Why did he let Chester die and spare him? His work must not be done.

When the pot of coffee was empty and the dogs were back inside, he wrote out his list of things to do for the day. With a heart that felt like an anchor, he slowly trudged up the brick pathway, one shaky step at a time, praying he didn't fall. With great effort, he reached the top of the hill, passed the tomatoes, some overripe and falling off the vine, and headed toward his truck. He knew what he needed to do.

Johnny flew over the hilltops, straight to Amos's house. He pleaded with him as if his life depended on it, to consider the supervisor position if nominated. "I will," he finally said, "as long as Antique won't give me a hard time." In seconds flat, the inspector was in Antique's parking lot, frantically explaining the situation and pleading for an exception.

The bishop knew the community needed Johnny to solve their problems. He got things done. Things had gotten better for them since he'd been around. Observing the sincere trouble in his friend's bloodshot, blue eyes, his notorious hardline stance softened if just for a brief moment. "I usually speak my mind, but in this case I will stay quiet."

Johnny was almost there. So close, he almost believed that Amos had sworn in as the temporary supervisor; just one more bishop was needed to give his blessing. One more. However, in all the years he'd helped out the community, he'd never met this man. He didn't know anything about him. How could he get a line to this man he didn't know and get his favor for Amos?

As his wheels turned and turned, he found himself at Mose's place to pick up another blueprint. There, he told Mose and Reuben about Chester's death, his idea to get Amos nominated as the interim supervisor, and the reason why. Though he had managed to get Antique's blessing—nothing short of a miracle, he lamented the unfortunate fact that he didn't know the last bishop at all as if it were the end of the world—his world.

"Oh, he's my uncle," Mose said, surprising the inspector. "I can talk to him if you want. It shouldn't be a problem."

Johnny stood shocked for moment, almost unable to believe his luck. *This is why I'm still here,* he thought. *It's all falling in place.* Elated, Johnny flew over to Amos's porch to tell him he got permission from the bishops, as if he had solved world hunger. Amos and Elsie could hardly believe it. Now, he needed to somehow get Amos nominated, but how? By the rules, the two remaining supervisors nominated candidates. He wracked his chemo brain for the answer, but nothing came to mind on that sad summer day.

He went home early. On the lawn mower he hoped inspiration would strike, but it didn't. He called Audra to tell her about Chester since she had been so interested in everything that was going on, surprised that Patti already had told her that morning. He didn't think Patti listened to anything he said. He ate a big bowl of vanilla ice cream and settled into his recliner in front of the sports network to watch a Phillies game, but even that only made him feel a little better. What was he going to do?

***

The next morning after taking his grandsons to their golf lesson, Johnny dropped them off back at home and drove up to Bart with Grace on his mind, intending to pay her a visit. When he got near her house, there were so many cars in the driveway he figured he'd just be an intrusion and turned around. At the end of the road he came upon his old buddy, Ned, the Bart Township road master, who was retiring the next year after forty years on the job. The old men slowed down their trucks and talked across their opened driver side windows.

"Hey, John. What are you doin' here on a Saturday?"

"Ned! How are ya, man?" he asked, putting on his happy face. "I just came up to see Grace, but I turned around when I saw all the cars. You heard about Chester?"

Ned said he had and asked Johnny if he knew anything about the funeral.

"The viewing's tomorrow night at 6:00, and the funeral is Monday at 2:00. I'm really gonna miss him," the inspector said close to tears, pausing to recover his composure. "Without Chester I'm afraid I might be lookin' for another job. Bill hates me and if he gets one of his friends in there to fill Chester's spot, they might just try to find another zoning officer."

201

"Bill doesn't hate you, John."

"You shoulda seen the way he was screamin' at me at the hearing!"

"Ah, he wasn't screamin' at you, John, he was screamin' at himself," Ned assured him. "He was mad because he knew it was all his own fault."

"Ned, man, you don't understand. I can't take any chances," Johnny said with desperate eyes. "I've got to find a good replacement. I'm hopin' I can get an Amishman in there."

"Ha!" He slapped his steering wheel. "John, you're dreamin'! That'll never happen—at least not in our lifetimes. The bishops would never allow it. You know that."

"Ned, I think I've got the bishops to agree to it and I think I've got Amos King talked into doing it."

"Are you kidding me?" he chuckled. "If you can actually pull that off it would be a first. I don't think there's ever been an Amish supervisor, at least not as long as I've been around. You know you have to get one of the two supervisors to nominate him though, right?"

"Yeah, I been wrackin' my brain, but I haven't come up with a way to do that yet."

"Why don't you talk to Eli Harnish?" the roadmaster suggested. "You know he's on the board, right? Everybody listens to him."

A car had turned the corner, came up behind Ned's idling truck, and waited there impatiently for a few long seconds, finally giving a couple short toots of the horn. Johnny sped away to find Mr. Harnish, sure that he held the key.

The inspector found the influential man at his farm and explained his idea, and the last piece of the puzzle that he needed to make it work. "Well, John, even if Amos is appointed as the interim supervisor, he would be required to run for reelection." Johnny realized even he couldn't maneuver a run for reelection, and his hopes sank like a golf ball in a water hazard.

***

Sunday evening Johnny attended Chester's viewing and tried hard not to think of himself lying lifeless in a box but couldn't help it. He fought back tears, which he blamed on his lack of male hormones. When he got to Grace at the end of the line that went by the casket, he gave her a big hug.

"You've got to keep fighting this, John," she urged through the waterfalls coming from her eyes. "I can't lose both of ya!"

"I will, Grace, I will," he promised, and drove home with a heavy heart.

The next day after Chester's funeral and before going home, Johnny stopped by Hometown Builders to say hello to Dan (who was still hobbling around) and to remind him, as he did Abe the week before, that they needed to get moving on their expansion project.

"Yeah, we know, we've just been so busy," Dan explained, a little harried. "You're still playin' for me in that tournament tomorrow, right?"

"Oh, man, I almost forgot about that." Johnny sighed and rubbed his bald head. "Yeah. Yeah, I can still do that." But he didn't want to. He wanted to save his energy for the golf tournament with his friends two days later, but he already gave his word. Home he trudged, not looking forward to the following day, and fell asleep in his recliner in front of the sports network.

***

The tournament round could have been a comedy show. Abe and the other guys hunted for their balls every shot, increasing their time on the course under the blazing, energy-zapping sun by at least 50%. Afterward, while the Mennonite men sat at their table in the clubhouse eating, the inspector limped through the buffet alone, completely worn out.

"Boy, you really had to carry those guys, huh?" chuckled another golfer who was filling his plate next to Johnny.

203

"Oh, God! You have no idea!" he muttered, thinking, *and I'm on chemo.*

Wednesday he woke up even more exhausted than when he went to bed, every joint of his body aching. He got his blood work done but didn't see his doctor or any of the nurses he knew. Grace still wasn't back in the office. Driving around Bart from inspection to inspection, he thought about Chester and lacked his former zeal. He even mentioned to one or two Amishman, that he might not be around long.

He had hoped the next day's golfing tournament with his friends would lift his spirits, but it didn't. Not only did he play like a Mennonite, he played like a Mennonite on chemo, unable to make his body or brain do what he wanted. He couldn't keep his balance long enough to hit his shots, and his mind kept wandering to the hearing decision that was to be that night, though he didn't know why. It wasn't like it was going to matter one way or the other. Chester was gone and Bill had it in for him.

Neither he nor Grace planned to attend the meeting, each so sick of the politics they could scream. That evening while Johnny sat in his recliner in front of the sports network watching the Phillies lose to the New York Mets 9-5 hoping it wasn't an omen, Gabriel Glick called twice. Each time the inspector let it roll to voicemail.

Chapter 23

End of August

Friday morning Grace was back in the office, and at 9:00 am Johnny walked through the door. Though he told himself he didn't want to know, convinced that with Chester gone it didn't even matter, he couldn't help but ask if she knew the hearing decision. Curiosity killed the zoning officer.

"No. They didn't leave one, and they usually leave one," she said, searching on her desk. "I'll see what I can find out." She called the attorney who told her he'd send the decision via fax or email, but neglected to reveal the requested information over the phone.

"Well," Johnny said, "I've got two messages from Gabriel on my voicemail that I haven't listened to yet."

"OK, so if he called you directly," Grace puzzled out, "he must have gotten what he wanted otherwise his attorney would have called."

Johnny agreed that her reasoning made sense, took a deep breath, and sat down to listen to the first of the two messages. When a smile spread across his face, Grace had her answer.

"He just called and said, 'I got everything I wanted. Thank you for everything!' " The inspector chuckled, heaved a heavy, sad sigh, and crossed his arms over his belly, gazing into the unfocused distance. A melancholy pause ensued with Chester on their minds.

"Well, it makes me more relieved than anything," Johnny said, breaking the silence. "At least common sense won over. If common sense hadn't won, that would just be the start of it and who knows what wudda happened. I could tell you I wuddn't gonna be a part of it!" Grace agreed wholeheartedly and watched as her zoning officer rose to his feet, inch by inch, careful to keep his balance. "Even as much of a pain in the backside as Gabriel is," he added during his slow ascent, "he did absolutely nothing wrong."

The interviews for replacement supervisors to be held that night crossed Johnny's chemo brain, but he didn't want to bring it up in front of Grace, sure she'd cry. Just thinking about it made his stomach turn, and any good feelings he had due to the hearing decision quickly faded as he walked out the door.

***

The weekend started off bad when, shortly after the sun rose, he stopped in his local Wawa for a coffee. Someone inside asked about his health and he ended up telling several people the whole story of his summer. His chemo brain lost track of time and didn't remember that he had left his lights on. He had to call Young John to come jump him again. He felt so low on energy, he didn't even take his grandsons golfing.

He was lonely, too. His wife had left the night before for a horse show a couple hours away that their middle daughter had organized and would be gone until Sunday night. His mother had caught a cold and forbid him to come over, afraid he'd get whatever she had and weaken him for his final chemo session on Wednesday. His friends were out of town and Audra wasn't answering. Young John and his wife were home, but they never came downstairs to see him unless they needed something.

He looked at the grass. With everything going on he had let it get higher than he ever had and every time he saw it, it only reminded him that things weren't like they used to be and might never be again.

He started up the mower, hoping it would clear his mind, but this time his worries took control. He worried about his future in the township and how his body would take this final chemo session coming up on Wednesday. Mrs. Fisher got so sick after her fourth session she quit and had been going downhill fast. Chester didn't even get to chemo. It was hard to believe. Just a month ago his friend and supervisor was fine, assuring him that nothing would happen to his position as long as he had anything to do with it. Now Chester was gone. Soon he might be, too.

He sat in front of the sports network in the air conditioning, too tired to do anything else, and allowed himself to feel sorry for his own situation just a little bit. A little turned into a lot, until he had convinced himself that no one cared about him, and especially not his son. Young John never had any response to any of the texts he sent when updating everyone about his health, nor did he ask him how he felt. Not even once. To top it off, his son forbade his children from even talking about his illness.

By the time Patti returned on Sunday night, Johnny's mood had darkened so much so, that when she walked into their living room to say hello, he pretended to be asleep. He didn't want to talk or even look at anyone. No one did any work but him, and *he* was the one on chemo. The whole weekend, while Patti was off playing, his son never once went outside to do anything around the house. He needed to get away, but his body wouldn't cooperate.

The next day he felt no better but trudged up the bricks anyway, unsure if he would even make it to the top. With his list in hand and much more on his mind, he stuffed himself into his cluttered vehicle and started it up. On the way out of the small development that used to be an open field in front of his old home, he passed by the little, yellow house on the corner and noticed a for sale sign out front.

Instantly, he began thinking of solutions instead of problems. Perhaps if he didn't live under his son and know everything he did and didn't do all the time, he wouldn't get so irritated with him. Living there might just solve everything. He would still be on the farm's original 174 acres, between both sets of local grandkids, and close enough to see the old barn where Patti still kept her horses, so that she would agree to live there. If the cancer took him like it took Chester, she would at least have a home of her own. Buying it would be ideal if not for a few problems: he had no credit, no bank account, and nothing in his name, having given it all away to his children. But if he could get that Wawa for Mose, it would be almost all the money he needed. Surely he could scrounge around for the rest.

He drove over to Mose's place to drop off another plan and pick up a blueprint. He wasn't sure if Mose remembered the figure he promised him but didn't want to bring it up again in case he had changed his mind. It had to work.

He parked and in his mind he bounced into the office—though his weary body dragged behind—and put on a happy face. "It's Mick Jaggeeeeer!" he shouted, greeting the man. They chit-chatted awhile about his health and Mose's latest blueprint, then in his excited and highly caffeinated persona, Johnny brought up the real reason for his visit that morning: Wawa.

"I just wanted to let you know I've got a lead on Wawa and I'm putting a call in today. Now, when I leave a message, if they are interested they'll call me right back," he predicted, confidently assuming that to be true.

Johnny carried the rolled-up blueprints to his truck, hobbling along, almost stumbling due to a loose piece on one of his worn loafers catching on the pavement. He started his truck, panned through his phone for his contact at Wawa that his golfing buddy had given him, and dialed. In Mose's driveway he idled and, with palms sweating, listened to the phone ring, rehearsing in his head what he wanted to say.

After the sixth ring an answering machine picked up and the greeting instructed him to leave a message after the tone.

"Uh... hello. This is John Coldiron. My golfing buddy, Paul Hess who works at Wawa's corporate headquarters gave me your number and said you'd be the guy to talk to. I've got a piece of property in Bart township in Lancaster County that would make a great spot for a Wawa. Give me a call."

He ended with his number and his habitual, "Talk to ya," and headed to Strasburg for another inspection. In five minutes, just like he predicted, his phone rang. His heart raced; his palms became slippery on the steering wheel. This was it. One of his problems would be solved. He pulled the truck over on the side of the road to answer just in case his cell reception died in the middle of the call; he didn't want to miss a single word.

"Hello?" he answered, his hands shaking.

"Hi. This is Greg from Wawa. I'm returning your call about a parcel in Lancaster county."

"Hey Greg. Thanks for callin' me back, man!" he said. "I hear you're a golfer.' Johnny didn't want to jump right into talking about business and figured if he could make friends with him, he'd be more likely to want to help him.

"I don't know if I'd call myself a golfer, but I do like to play," he said. "And you know Paul?"

"Oh yeah. He's one of my golfin' buddies," he exclaimed. Then in an effort to strengthen the deal he invited the man join them for a round.

Greg chuckled. "I'm not sure if my wife will let me," he said then got down to business: "So you have a parcel in Lancaster County, correct?"

"That is correct." Johnny's heart thumped audibly in his chest.

"OK. Let me give you the name and number of the person who handles that area." Johnny felt himself start to deflate. The Wawa Corporate employee proceeded to give him the information, which the inspector scribbled at the bottom of his list that sat, as always, on top of the giant stack of papers and books in the middle of his cab.

"Thank you very much," Johnny said, adrenaline still rushing through his body. He knew he didn't have the energy to wind himself up again for another pitch, so before he could come down too far, he dialed the number, got another answering machine, and left another message. He crossed his fingers and drove away to get some work done.

CHAPTER 24

September 2

The days were becoming noticeably shorter now. Every other year he mourned the passing of summer, his favorite season by a mile, but this year, like a friend who overstayed his welcome, he was glad to see it go. It had been a summer like none other in his life what with the chemo, Chester passing, and the trouble in Bart over the Nickel Mines project.

As he drank his last cup of coffee and filled out another permit application at his cluttered and cramped living room table, he heard Patti stir in her bedroom, getting ready to accompany him to his final chemo session that morning. She had gone with him to every chemo session and most of his other appointments, too. She had been by his side the whole time, putting her entire life on hold to help him through his illness, but it never occurred to him that she had. They didn't talk much; she hated when he retold his stories, but she was there like a wife was supposed to be, through sickness and in health.

He knew his friends had been there for him, especially Davy Huston, who kept his mind off his troubles by inviting him to round after round of free golf. As a special "thank you" to his friends and to keep his mind off what this last chemo session would do to him, he cooked up an alternate plan for Saturday night instead of going to a restaurant like Audra wanted and specifically to the Bullfrog Inn like Cheryl suggested when he told everyone his daughter's idea. His brainchild would save him money since he would have insisted on paying the bill wherever they went. He could invite John and Melinda and all the grandkids; maybe even his mom and Dolly would come. Brooke probably wouldn't attend, but he could at least invite her, too. It would be a big appreciation party to everyone who got him through the summer, but especially his buddies. He was pretty sure Audra wouldn't care.

Johnny and his wife arrived at his last chemo appointment to the doctor's office bright and early and, as usual, they were there before the staff took their positions. At 8:00 am on the dot, Paula took her seat behind the plexiglass, slid it open, and greeted the couple with a big smile.

"How ya doin' Mr. C?" she said with a friendly smile.

"I'm great!" he said, jerking his shoulders up in excitement. "This is my last chemo session, so I'm especially good today."

"You're last one? Congratulations, Mr. C., but man, I'm gonna miss ya. Who's gonna tell me stories about the Amish?"

"Well, as a matter of fact, my daughter—you met her last time I was in here for chemo, what, three weeks ago. Anyway, she's writing a book about all my experiences with the Amish."

"Oh, OK. You'll have to get me a copy. I'll give you my address," she said and started to write it down. "I was drivin' in Lancaster the other day and I saw the weirdest thing. It made me think of you."

Before Johnny could ask for details, she continued: "Yeah, I saw this regular lookin' kid about sixteen, in a baseball cap drivin' a cart, but it wasn't like the usual Amish lookin' one, it looked more like one you'd see giving tours in Philly, ya know? And beside him sat this teenaged Amish girl, bonnet and all!"

"They were probably on a date," Johnny said, "I tell ya, if an Amish girl gets asked out on a date by an English boy, she's goin'!"

"They are allowed to date boys who aren't Amish?"

"Oh, well, if the girl hasn't decided to be Amish yet, sure!"

Before Paula could ask another question, a patient walked in, and a nurse called Johnny into the doctor's office. After the nurse checked his vitals, she wheeled the cart with the laptop and blood pressure monitor back out to the hallway, closing the door behind her. Patti sat in a chair with her giant purse partially covering her belly, and Johnny sat on the padded table and leaned forward with his weight on his hands, waiting for the knock on the door.

When it came, instead of Dr. Caruso like he had expected, a young, slender, blonde woman walked in and introduced herself in a Russian accent. "Hello, Mr. Colt-i-ron," she said, squinting at her clipboard, "I am Dr. Yurchenko. I am here to interview you."

Johnny thought word must have gotten around about him.

"I need to ask you a few questions before we administer your final dose of chemo since most patients don't make it to their final session due to either death, or extreme sickness," ," she said matter-of-factly.

Johnny's eyes nearly popped out of their sockets. "Oh! No, I've been very fortunate. I haven't been sick," he said, thinking about poor Mrs. Fisher diagnosed at the same time as himself, now bedridden. Then, in his big, happy-fun voice he added, "I love that chemo stuff—I've been gearing up for it!"

She smiled quizzically, unsure how to interpret the man. "We still need to make sure you are well enough to take this last dose."

She went on to ask the questions on the form. How is your balance? Good. Have you had any tingling in your feet? Some. Have you felt nauseous? No. And so on until all the boxes on the paper were checked off.

"Did I get 'em all right?" he joked loudly with his sparse eyebrows lifted so high they looked like they might detach from his face. "Take me to the chemo. I'm not leavin' here without it!"

The young woman doctor looked at her patient, her fresh face hinting at a smile. "I was warned about you. They told me you were different."

Johnny started the arduous task of getting down from the table when Dr. Caruso poked his head in just long enough to deliver the news. "Did she tell you your PSA is down to 81?"

"No!" Johnny cried with a smile so wide it made creases inside of his creases. Dr. Caruso smiled slightly, tapped the door frame a couple times, and hurried down the hall.

"Oh, I'm sorry!" Dr. Yurchenko said, her cheeks turning pink. "I thought you knew!"

"No, I didn't, but that's OK!" Johnny chuckled. "Oh, Doc just gets a thrill out of this!"

With Patti following behind, the patient chuckled all the way to the chemo dispensing room for the final time. He made it. Maybe everything would be OK after all.

"Johnny!" he heard a familiar voice shout from behind. He turned and saw Lisa, the gregarious nurse from his very first unscheduled hook-up in Exton who, when he came two days later for a white blood cell boosting shot, went out of her way to say hello when she spotted him in the parking lot. It had made him feel so special, that, though he hadn't seen her since, he hadn't forgotten her.

She hadn't forgotten him either and came over to give him a hug. "I need your phone number," she said in front of his wife.

He flushed and giggled nervously, glancing sideways at Patti. "You do?"

"Yeah," she said, looking at him with a sly grin, "because if I ever get sick, I'm giving you a call. I want those people who were praying for you to pray for me!"

Johnny laughed big. However, deep down he believed those prayers from those people were the main reason for his remarkable recovery.

"We're not going to give him any credit," she added with a wink, pointing to Dr. Caruso who hurried by.

"Oh," Johnny said, still laughing, "I think we'll give him *some* credit!"

The patient sat down in the vinyl stuffed chair one last time with Patti at his side. Lisa hooked him up. He took out his phone from his pocket and texted Huston, Audra, John, Brooke, and Dolly the good news: "PSA 81 on last bag of chemo." He would have to call Frank and his mom on his way home.

As usual, Audra and Huston replied right away, but one person who hadn't responded to anything regarding Johnny's illness,

213

who seemed to refuse to even acknowledge it was even happening at all, texted back:

"That's awesome!"

Those two words warmed the old man's heart more than the chemo burning through his body. His son really did care. Content in the moment, he sat in the chair smiling, the poison coursing through his veins, killing the cancer. As the hour ticked by, his mind wandered to the rest of his day, his new weekend plans, then to Wawa. He hadn't heard back. *She must not have gotten the message yet; it's the perfect place.*

Audra interrupted his thoughts with a text: "Can you do me a favor? I have been trying to get up with Dan Stoltzfus to interview him for the book, and we've been playing phone tag. Can you ask him if he has any time to sit down with me while I'm there?"

***

A few hours later Johnny's phone rang. It was Audra again. She wanted to check up on how he felt before leaving the next day with her two kids, Quinn and Irie, for a visit. He happily reported feeling much better than he thought he would have and told her the story of nurse Lisa.

"It was just so cool to have her there at this last one since she was there at the first one," he said as if he suspected some sort of cosmic significance. He also casually ran his alternate idea for Saturday night by her:

"We could all go over to Frank and Aileen's basement," he started, because it's finished now—and Aileen's real proud of it—and she wants everyone to come and see it. I'm like, 'OK' but you know, it's just a basement. I still have to do the final inspection on it, and I can do that while I'm there, and John and Melinda can come, and Melinda can tickle the ivories—because, you know, Frank has a piano. He just started taking lessons—and all the kids can be there and maybe Mamaw can come, too, and Dolly. I'll have it all catered on my dime as a kind of, like, a 'thank you' to everybody for gettin' me through this summer."

214

There was an uncomfortable silence. "Uh... I don't know Dad," Audra said in her best disinterested tone. "Have you talked to Aileen about this yet?"

"Not yet, but I'm sure it won't be a problem." He continued on, trying to convince her that his was the better plan. "But... I don't know," he added, thinking out loud, "because Aileen's real funny about kids."

"Oh? Well, there would be a lot of kids over there, for sure!"

"Yeah," Johnny said, starting to rethink it, "she might not want all of them over there. I mean, they've got white carpet upstairs."

"Oh. Yeah, that sounds like she *definitely* won't like it," Audra said, trying to sound natural. "Maybe we should just stick with the original plan."

"Well, we'll talk more when you get here."

She agreed, hoping he'd eventually talk himself out of it since it sounded like he was halfway there anyway. "You're not going to Bart today, are you?"

"I'm here right now!"

"What? Dad, you are supposed to rest!" she scolded. "We're celebrating on Saturday, and you can't be dead tired and not want to go. This is the only time I'll have."

"I'm just doin' a couple things. Oh—I thought of another Amish story for the book that I didn't tell you. This one involves Amos King. It's a really cute one. This one time-"

"Save it until I get there tomorrow," Audra interrupted. "I want to record it to have your exact words."

CHAPTER 25

September 3, 4

Johnny sat in his recliner, intently studying his spiral-bound calendar when Audra arrived. As she walked through the door, he shouted her name in his happy, highly caffeinated persona like he hadn't seen her for years. Before he could get up, she rushed over to where he sat and gave him a big hug.

"How are you feeling?"

He had assumed the worst for his last chemo session and had planned to do as much sitting in the air conditioning as he could stand. It turned out, though, he couldn't stand to sit for long and went to Bart almost immediately after his session the day before. When he didn't have to run into any cornfields and woke up the next morning feeling passably well, he figured he dodged a bullet.

"I'm feelin' real good. I'm actually feelin' a lot..." he stammered, and in looking for the right word, bounced his shoulders up and down, "uh... *peppier* than I thought I would be."

Audra glanced at the calendar in his hands with big ex's through the days that had passed and asked why he had written her name in tomorrow's box with "Grace 1:00" beside it.

"Oh, I thought me and you could go out to lunch with Grace at the Hometown Kitchen tomorrow."

"Oh... I can't," she said, quickly.

He tried to hide his disappointment. "Why not?"

"Uh... Mom wants to go shopping with me tomorrow."

"She does? She didn't tell me that! But then again she doesn't tell me anything. Well, that's good." He felt glad since Patti craved attention, and she hadn't received much since he'd been sick. He figured she must be feeling pretty neglected with the star treatment paid to him that summer.

"You know, Dad, on the drive here, I was thinking about your new idea for Saturday night, but I think we should just go out to dinner like we had planned," she said, biting her lip.

He sighed, looking down at his calendar in disappointment but said nothing. Nothing was going his way, not counting his miraculous recovery, of course.

"I think all that with the basement and the catering and getting everybody together just sounds like too much work. You need to rest."

He reluctantly agreed, and in a bit of a huff he put down his calendar and sat back in the recliner. After all, it was supposed to be *his* weekend; he was the one who made it through chemo alive; his birthday was soon, and he should be the one to call the shots. He had to admit, though, dinner at the Bullfrog Inn would be easier.

"Why don't you invite Grace to dinner with us on Saturday night?"

"That's a good idea!" he said, his mood recovering if just for the moment.

Audra smiled. "I want to do another interview with you." She removed the books from the nearby director's chair and sat down, set the tape recorder on the recliner's arm, and pressed record.

"Tell me how it went yesterday."

"I thought I already told you."

"You did, I just want it on tape."

"Oh, OK." He went on to recite the stories about the Russian nurse, seeing Lisa again, and added John's surprise text reply, which he hadn't mentioned before. Then he got a little off track: "Oh, and get this," he said, rubbing his face in exasperation. "John called me the other day and asked me if *I* could cover one of *his* inspections!" When Audra asked why her brother couldn't do an inspection, Johnny said he didn't ask "because if it was for su'um stupid, it

217

would bug the livin' daylights out of me, and I'd just rather not know."

He talked a little longer about the job he covered for his son, then remembered the other Amish story he wanted to tell her when she had stopped him, wanting to get it on tape.

"Amos King, he has a daughter named Sarah. And they now live on White Oak Road, pretty close to Amos, but they used to live on Quaker Church Road, and they had called me up wantin' me to help 'em out. I think it was probably to help 'em out with gettin' the approval to put a house on White Oak, close to Amos. So I stopped over and saw Sarah and her husband, and, you know, we got to know each other and this and that. And Sarah was about nine months pregnant, and I was gonna do su'um for 'em, I can't remember what," he sighed and knocked on his head a couple times.

"So anyway, I get all the paperwork done, and I head over and knock on the door, and Sarah yells and says, 'Come on in, John!' I'm like, 'OK.' I walk in and Sarah's in the recliner. I say, 'Hey Sarah, I got that paperwork,' and I look over at the couch and here's this little baby laying there. And I said, 'Oh, my gosh!' I said, 'That is so awesome, it's so cute!'—a little girl. I said, 'That's just fantastic! How old's the baby?' 'Oh, a couple hours.' " Johnny slapped his hands on his knees, looked to the ceiling, and laughed.

"I'm like, 'You gotta be kiddin'!' I couldn't wait to get to my truck to get my phone, and I call Amos. I go, 'Oh my Gosh, Amos, you gotta see this little grandbaby of yours!' And he goes, 'John, you're outta control! I haven't even had time to get to the grandbaby yet!' " Once again Johnny threw his head back and laughed big.

"But, yeah, that was my baby story. 'Oh, a couple-a hours!' " he repeated and chuckled again. "And I never did ask her, but I think she had it at the birthing center and drove on back."

***

That evening he passed on going out to dinner with his family to watch an Eagles game. They were losing their last pre-season match, Johnny figured, thanks to not using any of their starters. That wasn't

218

the decision he would have made, and that thought only led to grumbling about how no one ever listened to him or does what he wants to do—except for the Amish.

At halftime he rose from his chair, every joint and muscle creaking and groaning like a rusty machine in need of oil. He hadn't been out of his chair since he had gotten back from Bart before noon. Although he knew he needed to rest and everyone told him so, he still felt lazy, like he needed to get up and do something. He decided to check on Jared, his autistic six-year-old grandson, sure he had stayed home with his mother and didn't go to the restaurant with Patti and Audra and the rest of the kids. The boy was probably playing on the half-finished playset in the front yard, he figured, and began the long, arduous trek there.

As he climbed slowly and carefully up the brick pathway past the echinacea flowers that had lost their petals and fresh, hopeful-looking black-eyed susans, he finally reached the front yard and was surprised to see everyone there. The big grandkids were pulling the little ones in Mia's pony cart like a rickshaw, running around and around in big circles laughing and squealing, while Audra and Patti sat in lawn chairs watching them with half eaten boxes of pizza strewn around beside them. Last thing he knew they were going to an Italian restaurant in town.

The women explained the reason for their change of plans: they couldn't bear to tear the kids away from such fun. Johnny understood completely, but Audra's six-year-old daughter, Irie, didn't. She stood between her grandfather and her mother and asked, "So, we aren't going to the party?"

Audra and Patti froze. Audra looked at her father who was distracted by the grandkids in the cart, and fussed at Irie under her breath.

"I'm not, Mom!" Irie said, loudly, "I thought we were going out to a dinner party tonight!"

"Oh!" Audra smiled, glanced at her mother's relieved face, then explained the change of plans for the night to the girl. Johnny didn't notice.

"OK!" Johnny announced. "I'm goin' back in!"

"Is halftime over?" his wife quipped. He confirmed with a smile, returned to his recliner in the bottom floor of the house, and plopped down to watch his team lose the rest of the game.

***

As he drove out of the development the next morning, the sight of the little, yellow house on the corner jogged his failing memory, and he realized that he hadn't heard back from Wawa regarding the message he had left on Monday. Figuring she was either busy or out of town, he decided to call again the following Monday if he still hadn't heard back just in case something happened with the message and it never got to her.

Ordinarily he would have headed over for a quick visit to his mother, but she said she still wasn't feeling well and still didn't want him to come over. He was concerned. Colds didn't normally hang on her this long, though she did sound fine over the phone, making him feel a little better. She was probably being her usual worried self and didn't want to take any chances that she'd get him sick. Hopefully she would feel better soon and he, Patti, Audra, and some of the grandkids could stop over to see her on Sunday after she gets back from church.

The first stop in Bart was to the Township building. Johnny wanted to make sure he saw his newly widowed co-worker before she left at noon for the weekend and included her in his birthday celebration on Saturday. He still would have rather had lunch at 1:00 pm and figured she would have, too, since Saturday would be a hard day for her. That was the day she wanted to have Chester's birthday party, and now he was gone.

"Hey Grace, do you want to come to dinner with me, Patti, Audra, and my buddies to the Bullfrog Inn tomorrow night?"

"Oh, yes!" Grace said with a big excited smile, her eyes sparkling, almost like she had expected the invitation, throwing Johnny for a loop. "That will be so much fun. Does this mean I'll get to hear all the golfing stories?"

"Probably so!" Johnny chuckled as he turned and took an

unstable step toward the exit. *She's probably just happy to get out of the house*, he assumed, trying to make sense out of her unexpected reaction. Almost out the door, Grace stopped him with news that an interim supervisor had been appointed: Tom Gray.

"Oh!" he screamed in delight, beaming. "I completely forgot about him. Wow! That makes me happy!"

"I thought you'd like to hear that, John. He's a good man," Grace smiled sadly, leaving Johnny to regret his joyful outburst. "Now you get outta here and don't work too hard. I'll see you tomorrow at The Bullfrog. Six o'clock, right?"

"That is correct!" he confirmed, and limped back to his truck parked just steps from the door. Though he didn't remember telling her the time, he figured he probably did and forgot. These days he felt lucky to remember his own name. No wonder he didn't even think about Tom Gray as a possibility for supervisor. Johnny especially liked the choice since he figured they both probably thought the same way, what with Tom being a "fire and brimstone" Baptist preacher. Maybe everything would be OK after all. Maybe Tom could talk some sense into Bill and everything would blow over.

The rest of the morning he zoomed around Amishland, crossing names off his list, all the while his phone ringing with calls for new business... which he let roll to voicemail. He was tired— tired of zig-zagging across the countryside, tired of working so hard for not much money and so little appreciation. The township should be thankful to him for charging so little for the zoning service he provided that had led to prosperity in the nearly nine years he'd been on the job, but they weren't; they—or at least Bill—wanted him gone. But he didn't want to stop working; his work wasn't done.

He paid a visit to Antique to check up on his health (he was doing much better) and to give him his own update. Dan wasn't in his office so he crossed into the Hometown Kitchen to remind Abe again to get moving on their expansion project. He wasn't in either. So, Johnny headed home through the twisty roads with a few lonely cornfields still standing on either side, and, as he dodged the last buggy of the day, thinking about his future employment, Wawa called back.

***

When he pulled up to the house, he was surprised to see Audra on the front porch with her laptop and asked why she wasn't shopping with her mom. She explained that they got the time mixed up. He staggered down the brick pathway. grumbling the whole way that they could have had lunch with Grace like he had originally wanted to, and leave it to Patti to get confused.

As he collapsed into his recliner to watch some sports, Audra bounced in the room wanting to know if he had asked Dan Stoltzfus if there was a time she could interview him.

"Oh, no, I didn't," he said, rubbing his face like he did when something slipped his mind, which had become a regular occurrence. "Hey, but we could go up there right now. We could go to his house. I know where he lives!"

"I can't now," she said, acting put out. "I'm going shopping with Mom! I've been waiting all day!"

"Oh, OK," he said, trying to hide his scowl and returned his focus to the TV. "When is she going to be back?"

"Supposedly any minute now."

***

Patti arrived shortly thereafter and left again with Audra. The whole time the women were gone, the kids played while his phone rang non-stop. He hardly got to watch whatever game he was trying to watch, having nearly given up on the Phillies. Hours later as Audra and Patti returned carrying plastic grocery bags, they announced that they brought home dinner, having picked up some deli food from the local grocery store. On the way to the kitchen they walked past Johnny who sat on the edge of his recliner. pouring over a list on his clipboard.

"Boy, a lot of things happened when you were gone," he said, bouncing in his seat.

"Did Wawa call you back?" asked his daughter nearly jumping out of her gardening shoes in excitement.

"Huh? No, no," he said, not ready to tell anybody about that. "I got, like, three calls about new jobs. One is for tomorrow, one for Monday, and one for later this week."

"Oh yeah. Where are they?" she asked a little too curiously.

"One's in York, one's in Lampeter, and the other one is in Georgetown." All were either in or around Lancaster County.

Audra asked, "Is the one tomorrow in Georgetown?" holding her breath for the reply.

"No, no. That one is on Monday. The one tomorrow is in York."

She exhaled and walked a few steps down the short hallway to the kitchen to help her mom dish out food for the kids. While unpacking the food, she informed her father that Dan Stoltzfus finally called her back, asked if she had any time this weekend to interview him. "I told him we'll be in Bart at 6:00 tomorrow night for dinner at the Bullfrog Inn, and he suggested we meet him at the Hometown Kitchen at 5:30."

Johnny chuckled. "Dan was probably wondering why we weren't eatin' at his place!"

***

At dusk after eating dinner on paper plates, sitting on the leather couch in front of the sports network, they all made their way to the front lawn on the still and clear September evening. Like the night before, they built a fire and watched as the kids roasted marshmallows around it.

"Your dad's been doing a lot more drawings since he lost his certification, haven't you, Honey?" Patti said, beaming at her husband.

"What? You lost your certification? Your building inspector's certification?" Audra said, her jaw unhinged, staring at her father

223

sitting next to her in astonishment.

"Yeah," Johnny said, looking straight ahead at the fire, trying to act cool.

"What? How? When?"

"Well, right after I was diagnosed," he started and took and deep breath, "there was just so much going on I just kinda forgot to renew it and didn't realize it. Derrick, my engineer, was actually the one who discovered it and called Grace to tell her," he explained bitterly. "She told him I had bigger fish to fry."

"What? What about all those inspections you were doing?"

"I can do them in some areas where they don't care because your brother still has his certification and he just signs off. I just can't do any in this one territory—Derrick's township where he's a supervisor."

"Derrick, your engineer? I thought he was your friend!" Audra asked, totally confused.

"They had a falling out," Patti explained like there was more to the story. Johnny stayed quiet. "But you can renew your certification, right?"

"Oh, yeah. Yeah. I can go up to the college tomorrow, probably, and do it, but-"

"Well, why don't you?" she pressed.

He sighed. "I'm not sure I want to, OK?" he confessed. The drama with the township had nearly broken him. Zig-zagging across the countryside was getting tiresome. He just wanted to golf and mow grass. Besides, if he didn't renew his certification Young John would have to work more, and that's exactly what he thought his son should be doing.

"So what are you doing tomorrow, Audra?" Patti asked her daughter, sitting across from her.

Johnny, staring at the fire deep in thought, didn't see the odd expression that she gave her mother. "I'm going to Philadelphia to Jenn's baby's party, *remember*?" she answered, drilling holes in her mother's head with her eyes.

"Oh, yeah. Right," Patti said with an embarrassed look that Johnny didn't see either.

"I think I'll be back around 4:00 or 4:30, in time to make it to dinner, but it's so hard to tell," Audra added.

Johnny broke out of his trance. "Oh, well you can just go straight from route one down to Bart."

"Uh... well, no," Audra stammered. "I'm coming back here."

"Why?" he asked, confused, knowing that was the long way around, and she could save time if she followed his directions.

"Uh... to pick the kids up."

"We can take the kids," he offered.

She turned to her mother who looked like a deer caught in headlights. Johnny didn't notice this either. "Yes... but... uh... you have to come *with* me."

"I do?"

"Yes. I can't interview Dan without you. It would be too weird," she said, scrunching her shoulders, acting uncomfortable. "I need you to be there with me."

Johnny regularly described Dan as one of the nicest people in the world and couldn't understand how he could possibly make anyone uncomfortable. Despite this, he asked no questions, agreed, and said nothing more about it.

Quinn, Zander, Irie, and Mia around the fire

CHAPTER 26

September 5, Day

The next morning Johnny had just returned home from an early morning inspection and was getting out of his truck when Audra pulled in behind him to drop off her kids. As Quinn and Irie shot out of the car and raced each other to his basement door, she asked her father if he'd already done his inspections, guessing that's where he'd been.

"Yep!" he said, and didn't notice his daughter's sigh of relief. "But I might have another in Bird In Hand today if the guy ever gets back to me." When she asked where exactly Bird In Hand was and he told her "in Bart, the next town over from Georgetown," he didn't notice the alarm she tried to hide either.

"So what time's the party?"

"What did you say?" Audra asked quickly, her eyes fixed on him in an odd way.

"What time is Jenn's party you're goin' to?"

"Oh," she said and took a deep breath and exhaled. "It's at noon."

"And you're leavin' now?" It was only 9:00 am, and Johnny knew it only took an hour and a half to get where she needed to go.

"Yeah, she wants me to pick something up for her on my way."

"Oh, OK," he said and smiled. "Have a good time."

He walked to the basement as he heard her drive away.

Around lunchtime with nothing good on any sports network, he got restless and decided to drive to Bird In Hand although his client hadn't gotten back to him. On the way he passed the Bullfrog Inn, which reminded him to make reservations for that night.

When the girl picked up, they bantered for a while, and he, being a regular, asked to reserve a table for ten at 6:00, explaining who all would be there, including Grace who the hostess also knew, and what exactly they would be celebrating.

"Oh, that's wonderful!" she said, happy to hear the good news about his health. But can you make it at 5:30 or 6:30? 6:00 is very busy for us."

Johnny sighed. "No, it's got to be 6:00," he said, then lightheartedly complained. "Please don't make me call everyone back to reschedule a time. I don't even think I can!" *If we were doing what I wanted to do, time wouldn't-a been a problem. We coulda gathered at Frank and Aileen's whenever we wanted.*

As he drove right by the Bart Township fire hall, he and the hostess decided that everyone coming could sit at the bar until a table became available. On the way back he drove past the fire hall again and didn't notice anything unusual going on.

***

"I just don't understand why Audra has to do all this running around while she's here!" Johnny grumbled to his wife from his recliner that afternoon as they waited for her to return. Patti just shrugged as she walked by him on her way to her bedroom but said nothing. He checked the clock next to him for the second time in five minutes and grew grumpier. *Where is she? This is ridiculous. We're gonna miss our reservations that I had to practically beg for. We shoulda gone over to Frank and Aileen's. I hope John and Melinda aren't mad that I didn't invite them. Catering would have been a lot less expensive. I just won't eat.*

"Johnny, you should probably take a shower," Patti shouted nervously through the apartment from her bedroom where she was brushing Irie's white-blonde hair.

"I don't want to take a shower," he barked back from his recliner.

"Well, can you at least put on a nice shirt?"

He sighed and struggled out of his chair to stagger through the french doors and into his bedroom where he kept his clothes. *Why in the world does she want me to dress up? She never tells me I need to dress up any other time. She's being bossy just like Audra. They are just alike. We're not doin' what I want to do. It's all about them and what they want. They don't even care what I want. Now I'm not even allowed to wear what I want. No one ever thinks about me. Things never go the way I want. No one appreciates how much I do for them.*

He put on a shirt with a pocket, plopped back down in his recliner in front of the sports network, and stewed.

***

At 4:45 Johnny saw his daughter finally cross the bay windows and enter Patti's bedroom door. He began his slow and laborious ascent to the upright position.

"Sorry, Dad," Audra shouted from the hallway. In she walked to the living room, harried, with excuses on her tongue: "It always takes longer to get back from Philly than I think." Much to Johnny's chagrin, she rattled off a list of things she still had to do before leaving again for dinner.

At 4:5 in a not-so-happy voice and a face to match he asked, "Are you ready to go?"

She looked at her mother. "Do you have any makeup?"

Johnny sighed in exasperation and slumped back down in his recliner. *Women. She should have left sooner.*

After three minutes of makeup application, she walked back into the living room and announced she was now ready to go.

"We're going to be late!" Johnny grumbled out loud with a scowl, limping toward the door.

Audra looked at the time on her phone. "I thought you said it takes a half an hour to get there."

228

"It does. It's 5:02."

"Well, my phone says 4:58. We're actually going to be a little early for Dan's interview at 5:30, and we'll make our reservation at 6:00, no problem," she said, chuckling quietly at her father's grumpiness and suppressing a smile. In a half an hour he would be happier than he had ever been in his life if he doesn't have a heart attack. They walked up the brick pathway as Irie and Quinn skipped ahead.

"Are we going to take two cars?" Patti asked, bringing up the rear.

"Yeah," Audra answered, "because my kids and I will go straight to Mamaw's after dinner."

Johnny started to walk toward Patti's car where the kids waited inside impatiently.

"No, Dad, ride with me," she insisted. "I've got really good air conditioning! You can tell me more stories on the way."

He sighed again, and walked toward the passenger side, the scowl still plastered on his face, thinking about how bossy Audra had been the whole time she'd been visiting.

"Dad, check this out." In the palm of her outstretched hand lay a small digital recorder she had bought at Walmart the day before. "I'm going to interview Dan with this, so you can tell me all about how you met him on the way." She turned on the recorder and dropped it in his shirt pocket.

As predicted, the closer they got to Bart and the more Amish stories he told, the brighter his mood became. Audra had to ask the way and expressed her nervousness about the interview, which he found odd. He didn't find it odd that she was nervous about dodging the buggies up the narrow hills; even he had to admit, *that* takes some getting used to.

"See that farm over there?" He pointed in the distance. "It went up for sale right when I was first diagnosed, and Joel, the Amishman who owns it, called me because he got something in the mail from a surveyor he didn't understand, and he needed me to read it. I went up there to read his mail—but I had to wait until five o'clock at night—and I met him in his buggy.

229

"See, their boy is gonna sell the farm and move to New York, and him and the wife are real upset about it because it was their farm. And we're going to subdivide two acres and get them a house on that two acres so they can continue to live there.

"He set with me, and he says, 'John,' he says, 'My dad bought this farm in 1955, and my older brother farmed it for five years and I've been here ever since. This is hard.' I tried to tell him maybe good will come out of it. I said, 'This is your boy,' I says, 'Look at the farm down there,' I said. 'It's in terrible condition.' He says, 'Yeah, I know.' He says, 'How's he going to survive up in New York, John. He can barely keep the pipes from freezin' here!' I said, 'Well, that's his problem, not yours.' I said, 'He needs to go and find his way and you need to let him. You are not physically'—he's older than me—and I says, 'You are not physically capable of getting that farm back to life and fixing it.' He says, 'Oh no.' And I says, 'Neither am I. Sometimes you just gotta sell and move on, and is it hard? Absolutely.'

"And I told him the story about your mom. 'We sold our farm to my daughter,' I said, 'and my wife couldn't leave the house. It was years before she could leave the house. It was ridiculous!" he cried. "Everything worked out, but it was somewhat of a price, but, daggone it, it ended up fine,' I said, 'and it will be fine for you guys, too.' " He smiled and sighed. "So I end up being their counselor, the Roving Bishop."

They rode a few miles more, through a couple intersections backed up with buggies, and Audra saw a familiar landmark. "Oh, there's the little bank you like to go to," she said, recognizing the tiny, brick building barely big enough for two tellers with a large drive thru.

"Yep. I stopped there yesterday to tell Wanda that Wawa said no."

"Oh, no! Wawa said no?" Audra said, surprised that he had heard back and didn't tell her.

"Yeah," he said with only a hint of disappointment. "When I told Wanda she was... well... she wants her su'um to get coffee in, and she goes, 'John, I don't have a lot at this corner!' " he chuckled

230

once and sighed.

"Why did they say no?"

"They said there wasn't enough traffic."

"Does that count horse and buggies?" Audra joked.

Johnny laughed. "I shoulda said that! But I told her, 'The owner is Amish and *very* well-heeled.' And she goes, 'Oh, really?' I said, 'And they are builders and probably would pay for and build it themselves!' She laughed and said, 'I'm sorry. We have to have at least a traffic count of forty.' I said, 'Well, maybe a Reuters would work better.' "

"What's a Reuters?"

"It's a place like Wawa but in more rural places. And she goes, 'Oh, yeah. Reuters would be better.' So, that's what I'm gonna do. Reuters would be just as good. Mose said Reuters or Wawa."

Audra kept track of the time and it couldn't have been better, even down to the second. They dodged another buggy and Johnny told her that "after a while you'd get used to it. It becomes like second nature."

He sighed and thought about how different things were just a few months ago: he was inspecting houses with his son, Chester was still around, and he thought he'd have his zoning job until the day he died. He laughed to himself how that last one was still a possibility, only now more immediate.

"Now, you're comin' up to a stop sign then you'll go straight through where those cars are," Johnny instructed. As they stopped, he pointed out the corner where Antique would always stand to direct traffic when the siren went off. "Dan's gonna wonder why we're not eating here at his restaurant."

They drove on slowly toward their destination mere yards away. As they got closer, Johnny spotted a familiar face standing on the other side of the road, outside the fire hall instead of in the restaurant like he had expected. "Hey, there's Dan! He's right there!" he said, pointing to his bearded, bespectacled friend. Dan waved the cars over to where he stood; Audra turned in to park with Patti following right behind.

Dan waited anxiously as Johnny opened the car door and

struggled to get out. "I told her, you's gonna be wonderin' why we're not eatin' in the restaurant!"

"Oh, well, we can't meet in there either! Too many people. A big bus come!" Dan said quickly, like he was nervous about something, though Johnny didn't notice.

"Oh, gosh. That's good!"

"Yeah. A big bus come and… and Antique wants to see you anyways, so…" he said, edging closer to the road side entrance of the building.

"Wants to see who?" Johnny asked.

"You! And… your daughter. She'll get 'em in one shot. And my wife." Dan moved his friend toward the door as Patti followed behind Audra with Irie and Quinn. "How are you feelin' today?"

"Yesterday I was good. Today I been… a lil' different."

"Well, let's get you outta the sun," Dan said, though at 5:30 the sun was low and the temperature pleasant on that fifth day in September.

"Yeah. That's the big thing. And other than that I'm real good," he said as Dan opened the door to the sound of a buggy jangling by. "But man, I tell ya, that sun…" He stepped over the threshold and into the dark hall. Amos flipped on the lights.

"Surprise!" the full house of over a hundred people shouted in unison followed by cheers and laughter.

Horse and buggies parked behind the fire hall (photo by Adam Kegley)

CHAPTER 27

September 5, Evening

The crowd burst into a spontaneous round of Happy Birthday as Johnny stood motionless, jaw unhinged, not quite understanding how he could be staring at so many familiar faces. Patti, Irie, and Quinn filed in behind him as Dan and Audra stood at his sides. "What in the world is going on?" the guest of honor wondered aloud, both hands on his flushed cheeks.

The long-awaited moment had arrived and, amazingly, everything worked out perfectly. The hall, filled to capacity with Amish and English, looked spectacular. Johnny gazed in wonderment at the eighteen round tables that sat six a piece, decorated like a golf course with one "hole" for each, a friend or relative in every seat. A few tables lacked a centerpiece: an orange flag with five white and orange helium balloons anchored by a pint-sized cup filled with candy on top of green felt surrounded by four golf balls; so many people had arrived, more tables had to be set up.

Audra hugged her overwhelmed father, who hadn't moved a muscle, still trying to figure it all out. When the song ended the crowd of smiling faces waited in silent anticipation for the man they all came for to say something.

"I'm flabbergh…," he started and couldn't finish.

"Speech!" Huston shouted from a table in the front.

"No… I…," Johnny started again, and again couldn't

complete.

Amos King, leaning on the wall close by, called out, "John lost for words? Never before!" causing a round of laughter from everyone in the hall.

Johnny stammered one more time: "I... I... I don't know what to say," and laughed nervously, looking around in disbelief, staggering a few steps closer to the buffet table loaded with food (mostly provided by his mother who cooked so much her refrigerator couldn't keep up). "I... I was supposed to have dinner tonight and... Oh, gosh. Everybody's here. Oh, this is incredible. Oh, my God. Listen, I love you all. I love you all and this has been really trying..."

As Johnny gushed and attempted to gather his thoughts, Young John walked to where his father stood and handed him the wireless microphone that had been on the podium on the other side of the room. Into the mic he spoke, still looking around and wondering if he were actually in a dream. "But this is so unbelievable, I... I've never had anything like this!" he giggled, "That Dan Stoltzfus, he's no good!" He assumed that Dan had been behind it all. The audience laughed and he continued:

"I wanted to have dinner to make sure I said to my buddy Davy Huston," he said then looked at his long-time friend sitting at a nearby table. "You've carried me all summer and you've been real special. You've kept me... you've kept me in the loop, and I really appreciate that." He turned again to the general audience. "But the strength that I drew from all you people is... is what did it. It was your prayers that saved me.

"And this week—I gotta tell ya this story, of course. You shouldn't have given me a microphone." The crowd giggled. "When I talked the doctor into giving me chemo that first day, he said I had to do it quick, and I said, 'Well, quick would be right now.' So he hooked me up, and they had a nurse named Lisa—and she was a real sweetheart. She kept sayin' to me, she kept sayin', 'It'll work out, John, it'll work out.' She was tryin' to console me. And I told her, I said, 'Listen, I know everything's gonna work out because there's a lotta good people prayin' for me.'

"Well, this week when I took my last chemo, as luck would have it, Lisa was there, and I hadn't seen her since that first day," he said and started to chuckle

. "So when I get out from the doctor and I go by the desk with the nurses, Lisa yells over and says, 'Hey John! If I ever get sick I'm gettin' a hold of you!' And I'm like, 'What?' And she says, " 'Cause I want those people you had prayin' for you, prayin' for me! They're good!' " The crowd laughed and waited for more. "And she says, 'We're not going to give the doctor any credit.' And I said, 'No, we'll give him credit, too!' The crowd laughed as he looked from face to face.

"But this is... this is... unbelievable!" he giggled excitedly. "Thank you all. I... I... I...," he stammered at a loss for words again as the applause began.

Cheryl took the microphone, announced that they'd eat first and roast Johnny later, then pointed out the location of the plates, food, and drinks. She suggested Johnny and Patti start, so Patti grabbed a plate. Johnny did not. He was too overwhelmed and eager to talk to everyone to eat. Over and over he could be heard saying the same things: "This is unreal!" or "This is unbelievable" and once remarked that "everyone from my entire life is here!" Family, new friends, old friends, and those he'd lost touch with years ago, Patti, Ruth, Audra, Young John, Melinda, Dolly, all his grandkids, his brother Randy, Diane, aunts and uncles, cousins, their children, Grace, Huston, Cheryl, Frank, Aileen, and all his golfing buddies, even old softball pals and their wives attended. Dan and Liz, Mose, Amos and Elsie King, Antique, his wife, Marvin and his eight kids plus his extended family, Abe and Catherine, Leon Stoltzfus and his family, Ivan and Mary, Roadmaster Ned, Jenn, and so many others gathered as well. Even Brooke eventually showed up.

"Who did this?" he asked Dan and Liz at the first chance he got, still having no idea who the mastermind was, but beginning to suspect it wasn't Dan.

"It was your daughter, Audra!" Liz said. "She did it. She pulled it all together. She did a good job!"

"Yeah. It was startin' to get the best of her," Dan added, "It

235

was time to get it over with! She called me a couple of months ago, and we'd been emailin' about it ever since. We were afraid it wasn't gonna work out! I've been lookin' forward to this. Oh, youda had to tie me up wit' chains to keep me out!"

"Oh! If I had-a known!" Johnny said, shaking his head. "She knows I would not have been in favor of this whatsoever."

"We were in favor of it!" Liz said happily.

"Listen John," Dan teased, putting his hand on his friend's shoulder, "there comes a time when you have to listen to the kids!"

"She was here all day doing all of this," added Liz.

Johnny looked around in amazement at the plethora of people in attendance for him. "It's just… unbelievable!"

"John, did you see this?" Liz asked, pointing to the centerpiece cup.

"Oh my goodness!" Johnny exclaimed and laughed a big laugh, throwing his head back. "The Roving Bishop's Vanilla!" Empty customized pints of a fictitious Ben & Jerry's ice cream flavor served as the base for the flagpoles on each table. "Where's… Is Antique here? There he is!" He laughed a big excited, frenzied laugh and turned toward his favorite bishop. "I gotta get him! Right now!"

Johnny shouted across the hall cupping his hands around his mouth: "Hey Antique. Did you see what that says down there? Huh?" He lifted up one of the cups on the nearest centerpiece. Antique read it and giggled as he and his wife approached their overwhelmed and honored friend.

"You're special. I love you, man," Johnny said and laughed through another wave of joy that washed over him.

"The Roving Bishop?" Antique's wife read and looked at her husband, quizzically.

"Yeah!" Johnny explained, deliriously happy. "One day he said to me, he said, 'You're like The Roving Bishop!' " Johnny threw his head back and laughed and held his belly.

"You said that?" she asked, looking at her husband.

"Tell ya what, I gotta watch it with what I say around you don't I?" he laughed. "You know, I got a letter from your daughter inviting me months ago," he confessed.

"Oh, really? She's bossy, isn't she? Oh my God! She must have worked her backside off just to do this! Unbelievable!"

"Did you expect this, John?" the lady asked.

"Expect?" Johnny said as if that had been the furthest thing from his mind. "I thought we were goin' over to the Bullfrog Inn for dinner!"

"Should we go get you a couple drinks?" The bishop asked in jest causing those around him to laugh at the absurdity that Antique would deliver alcohol.

"Honest to goodness, I had enough money in my pocket for the folks that I mentioned when I first came in… I had enough money in my pocket to pay everybody's meal because I owed 'em."

"Now you're gonna really owe 'em!" Antique said. Those standing around cracked up at the quip and could barely catch their breath for a few moments.

Antique's wife asked the date of his actual birthday and he told her "September 12," adding that it was the same day as Chester's. He went on to explain that Grace had planned a surprised party on this same night before he died and she had wanted him to be there. "I said, ''Don't you worry. Unless the Good Lord takes me, I'll be there!' "

"And he took Chester," Antique said.

"Yeah, and he took Chester," Johnny said suddenly solemn and quickly changed the subject. "And Grace. You know, that's what Grace wants my daughter to make the title of the book, *The Roving Bishop.*"

The crowd that had gathered around the bishop and the man of honor laughed.

"Really? *The Roving Bishop?*" Antique said, shaking his head, embarrassed by the attention. "Do you realize how much trouble I'm going to be in this whole evening because of you? You're gonna have to visit me every day!"

"It's all love, man," Johnny assured him. "It's all love!"

An Amish woman a few years his senior pulled him aside to show him the birthday card she had for him. "Look," she said, opening it and holding it in front of him, pointing to a signature. "Mom signed it. Her birthday is tomorrow. She'll be 92. She wanted to be here tonight but she wasn't feelin' good. She wanted me to make sure you saw the card."

"Oh, you know I love Mom," Johnny gushed.

The lady laughed. "She loves you, too, John, and she hopes you get better. We all do."

Next, Johnny made his way to the table by the podium where his son, Melinda, and all his grandkids sat.

"Hey!" he said to the children. "Did you guys know about this?"

"I knew about it!" his oldest granddaughters, Brittany and Mia, said in unison.

"I've known about it for two months," the 11-year-old Quinn said with a smile.

"Well, why didn't ya tell me?" Johnny asked them all in his silly teasing voice.

"Granddad," Zander said in his robotic voice, "I would have told you, but I actually didn't know about it until we were in the van on our way here!"

The whole table burst into laughter.

As Johnny made the rounds, over and over guests asked if he suspected anything. He hadn't. He had been completely surprised and, most importantly, didn't have that heart attack as his wife had feared. Other guests, noticing he hadn't eaten anything, offered to get him plates of food, but he turned them all down, too excited and overwhelmed to take in any sustenance.

When it was time to cut the cakes, Aileen called Johnny over before she sliced into them so he could see them whole.

"Well, here they are. I want you to appreciate them," she said, waving a hand over the two giant cakes, one chocolate, one vanilla. He laughed at the slogan, "Many rounds to go!" with a golfer in icing on top of both. She took a picture before cutting into the vanilla, which he chose for the first slice.

"Did you have anything else to eat yet, Johnny?" she asked in a motherly way. He said he hadn't had anything yet, but he'd take a

238

piece of cake and eat it later.

"Speaking of eating, did you have somebody call the Frog and tell them we weren't coming?"

"Yeah. Yeah, Grace took care of it. She said she went over there today to pick up a gift certificate and the hostess said, 'We'll see you tonight!' She said she came here when Audra was setting up —doggone you guys—and confirmed that we were not having dinner at the Bullfrog Inn and went over to cancel them." He laughed and shook his head.

"Now which one is Grace again? Is Grace the one in stripes?" Aileen asked, pointing to the woman at a nearby table. Johnny confirmed that it was.

"And this was…" he started slowly, his mood changing, "She had planned to have a surprise party for Chester on this day."

"I know," Aileen said matter-of-factly while cutting the cake. "Except it wasn't going to be. It was never going to be. It was always for you."

Johnny, completely shocked for the second time in an hour, said in a near whisper: "Get outta here. Are you serious?"

"That's why when that happened…"

"Oh my God."

"When that happened, Audra had to come up with another idea to get you here, so she came up with the interview idea instead."

His mind was blown. Again he was rendered speechless, his head spinning, and felt grateful when, in that moment, Wyatt and Annabelle came over to show him how strands of hair would stand straight up after rubbing a balloon over them.

He smiled at his static-headed grandchildren and turned back to Aileen. "It's been a long summer, but it's been… You find out a lot about yourself, and a lot about the people around you. And you know what? That's maybe worth everything."

He made his way to the buffet, still chocked full of food, and made himself a plateful of fried chicken, mashed potatoes, green beans, and Italian fruit salad. His brother, Randy, walked up beside him.

"You know, Mom called me up because I was taking her here, and she told me to bring the biggest vehicle I had to pick her up since she had a lot of food to bring. And I'm thinkin', 'C'mon. How much food could she possibly bring?' And it almost didn't all fit in my SUV! I couldn't believe it!" He chuckled and continued. "You know, and that's why you weren't allowed to come over for the past couple of days. She didn't want you to see all the food she was cooking."

Johnny shook his head and chuckled at everything that went on without his knowledge as he took a seat at a nearby table with Patti. As he began to inhale his dinner, hungrier than he realized, Audra spotted him and came over with a big smile on her face.

"I got you!" she said triumphantly, wrapping her arms around his neck. "I thought for sure you were going to bust me that day I called Hometown Builders and you were there. What were the chances of that?"

Johnny looked confused then remembered the moment. "Oh! *That's* why you were calling?"

"Yeah. And that's why I had been talking to Grace. They were all in on it," Audra explained as her friend, Jenn, stood at her side.

"So I guess, she wasn't at your house this afternoon either?" he said to Jenn who just shrugged.

"All lies!" he cried with a grin. Then, taking a bite of cake and with his mouth full he said, "I guess if I were smarter I woulda picked up on it, but I had no idea. Now, I did think it was a little odd, that when we were on the way here, you said you were nervous about interviewing Dan for the book. He's the nicest guy God's ever made!"

"Have you seen the quilt yet?" Audra asked. "It's amazing."

"Quilt for what?" he managed to say after swallowing.

"You!"

"For me?" It was yet another surprise for the evening.

Audra led her parents to the auxiliary room where the quilt with fabric pens on top lay spread out on a couple of rectangular tables. "When Cheryl and I were here setting up today, she asked me if I had a guestbook. I didn't. We were just going to have everyone sign the poster of your caricature that she brought," she said, referring to the framed drawing of an old golfer from behind, lining up his shot, with "J.D." printed beside his oversized bottom. "But when Dan and Liz showed up, they said Elsie King was bringing a quilt she made and wanted everybody to sign it. It was perfect!"

Ruth, Audra, Patti, and Johnny stood by admiring the quilt with twelve large white squares over a red background bordered by yellow and then dark green. One large flower stitched in yellow and red filled each of the white squares, with the signatures of the party attendees inside the petals, more signing all the time.

"Oh, look what's written on top!" Ruth said, delighted to read it out loud. " 'John, we got you covered.' Now, ain't that purty!"

He looked with wonder at Elsie who stood by the doorway and asked her if she made it. She explained that her mother made them with pieces picked up at yard sales and sold them to raise money for the school. This one she had bought. He loved the thoughtfulness of the quilt to begin with, but now that it had such a great story behind it—even having in some way supported the Nickel Mines school—he loved it even more.

"What do you think?" Elsie asked with a smile.

"Are you kiddin' me? It's… it's…," he stammered, shaking his head in a vain attempt to rattle the words free. "I'm gonna end up cryin'," he said, laughing.

"They ain't everybody signed it," Ruth pointed out in her hillbilly way. Alarmed by this information, Johnny rushed for the microphone on the podium like it was an emergency, wading through a sea of people eager to talk to the night's celebrity if just for a moment. "Happy Birthday!", "Did you have any idea?", "How are you feeling?", "You look great," they said as he hurried by. Finally, he reached his destination and made the announcement:

"Excuse me," he said. The noisy crowd instantly hushed at the sound of his familiar and commanding voice. "I just got the opportunity to see the quilt that Elsie King put together, and I want to make sure that everybody signs it," he said, desperately trying to keep it together but starting to crack. "It'll be the thing I keep to my grave. So please don't walk out until you get your name on there!" The last few words were nearly drown out in sniffles and tears.

Audra followed her father's announcement by taking the microphone, thanking everyone for coming and inviting anyone who wanted to, to get up and share a funny or meaningful story about her father. Grace immediately jumped up and told the story of how, when Chester was sick, Johnny had offered to go with him to his doctor's appointment, confident he could get him hooked up to something, "even if it was an exhaust pipe!" The crowd laughed awkwardly knowing it had only been a couple weeks since her husband had died.

Several long moments ticked by before anyone took the microphone again, but for Johnny time stood still and flew by all at once. Johnny sat down again with his wife to continue his meal. A few people who meant to just stop by briefly got up to leave and passed by the man of honor to say goodbye. One Amishman asked if he was retiring, which reminded him of the problem with the township that hadn't crossed his mind all night. "No, I'm not retiring," the zoning officer explained. "I'm stayin' on as long as the supervisors allow me to." And in that moment, he meant it.

"You know this isn't just a birthday party, it's an appreciation party!" another Amishman said when he came by to shake hands on his way out. With that simple comment, Johnny's heart swelled. He looked around the room with new eyes, realizing, for the first time, how much he was truly appreciated—and not just by the Amish—but by everyone in attendance that night.

It was one of his golfing buddies who broke the ice for the second time. He stood in front of the still mostly full house and told the story of the first time he met Johnny on the golf course. He was followed by another, then another, then another who told the Gorilla Sundae story, then Cheryl, then Frank, then Davy Huston took the mic. He told of how they met trying out for the same spot on the local softball team, how long they'd known each other, what Johnny meant to him, and then paused a long moment to steady his voice.

"When I was going through what Johnny's going through, he would ask me every day how I was doing. I just wanted to make sure I did the same for him. We love you, Johnny." He then invited his friend to get up and say something. The crowd applauded, encouraging the guest of honor (who needed no encouragement) to take the mic. He rose and floated toward the podium, high on love.

"Tell the U-Haul Story!" Grace yelled from her nearby seat. "I don't think they can handle the U-Haul Story!" he replied, sparking laughter. For forty-five minutes he spun tales of the Prime Rib at Pinehurst golf course starring his Uncle Gene and the runs, then by popular demand, Huston and the U-Haul, then another and another, leaving his audience in stitches.

Then his tone changed to one of seriousness and solemnity. "You know, ever since I started on as the zoning officer here in Bart the day the girls were shot in the school, Grace over there would say, 'John, you were put here for a reason, you know that?' Well, I finally agree with what's been said. I was put here for a reason. But it wasn't for you Amish, or the community, and it wasn't even for the girls in the school," he said, looking around at the many smiling faces staring back at him: his friends, his family, and all the women in bonnets and bearded men in suspenders who had become like family.

"It was for me. Your prayers saved my life. I love each and every one of you and thank you all again for coming." He left the podium in a hurry before the tears of joy fell.

At the end of the night, while guests filed by Johnny for one last well wish and to say goodbye, the entire crowd of remaining Amish folk (headed up by Marvin), cleaned up the hall. Audra helped Patti pack up their little, orange car with the quilt, gifts of preserves from the Amish, and many, many cards and envelopes, then repacked the centerpieces into her own car. The leftover fried chicken and balloons were given to Marvin and his children before he turned off the lights and locked the door.

Johnny emerged from the empty hall, a smile plastered on his face, and joined his wife and daughter parked out front. Audra marveled at the night:

"When I walked in, I had no idea what to expect. Everybody kept asking me how many people were coming, and I was like, 'I don't know—100, give or take 50?' Dan didn't know how many Amish were going to show up; I didn't know how many of your friends were coming because this is Labor Day Weekend, and I knew a lot of people would be on vacation. I do know that Amos and Elsie King rescheduled their vacation and Nemo came back early from the beach just to be here. Seeing that full house was just amazing," she said, shaking her head in awe. "Everything went exactly like I'd hoped. How often does that happen?"

"It was…" Johnny paused, gazed up dreamily into the night as if the right word would be written in the stars, and found it. "Perfect."

Johnny seeing the filled house for the first time (video still by Diane Cavender)

Johnny and Patti (photo by Aileen Parrish)

Johnny telling the party attendees the story about nurse "Lisa"
(photo by Patti Coldiron)

Johnny telling a story to the party attendees.

EPILOGUE

September 6 – January 3, 2016

By the following morning Johnny still hadn't come down from his cloud. He climbed into his little pickup truck and drove to the nearby Wawa to get a coffee. Alone in his cab next to the stack of code books, forms, and lists, he allowed the tears of joy to fall, moved by the show of affection of so many people at once the night before.

Sitting on the leather couch in his basement living room next to Audra and Patti, he opened his cards and presents one by one, some touching him so deeply, more tears of joy fell despite his attempts to stop them. Halfway through the pile he chuckled and looked to his daughter. "I was about to say, 'I wish you hadn't done that,' but I can't. It was incredible." He paused.

"But I already have regrets," he said, lowering his head, shaking it. "I didn't mention my family." He realized that the two people sitting beside him had been there with him all along, but especially his wife who sat still and remained silent. "This whole summer has been just, gosh. with the chemo, and Chester, and the Nickel Mines hearing… One I will never forget."

On Monday he went back to work in Bart and all everyone could talk about everywhere he went was the party. Johnny thought one Amishman was going to cry right in front of him when he told him he wished that he could have been there but had found out about it the day after.

An Amishwoman, Marvin's mother, told Johnny how, at the

party, Audra was so happy to see Antique, she gave him a big hug right in front of her while the bishop stood rigid with his arms straight down at his sides. Johnny thought that was the funniest thing he had ever heard and that story became the latest one on heavy rotation, especially whenever Antique was around. A few weeks after the party, still high on life, he heard that Mrs. Fisher died, but he couldn't feel sad. He felt lucky.

In the beginning of October, still feeling lucky despite the Phillies ending with the worst record in the Majors, he had his one month post-chemo follow-up. Aside from the prayers, the question of whether the chemo or the Lupron had been responsible for the drop in his PSA remained. At his appointment he had his answer when his "bad blood count" went down to 56.

He began charging for consulting (all the extra things he had done for customers anyway: zooming around to get the prints, forms, checks, and permits, and delivering them to the customer's door), and handed over all inspections to Young John, which included anything having to do with Gabriel Glick. "You might as well get to know him," he told his son. "He's the largest landowner in Bart and the biggest taxpayer." After all, he still had the little bit of zoning money coming in.

His luck ran out, though, when Bill Herman noticed the front yard to the house next to the Hometown Kitchen being torn up—part of Dan and Abe's expansion project—and inquired. He scoured the code book and found an obscure rule, one Johnny had overlooked, obviously being violated. He immediately called the zoning officer to express his disapproval, loudly. Johnny rushed to the place where Abe and Dan, away in New York on a hunting trip, had scheduled the paving, and stopped the production minutes before they were to begin.

It didn't matter. Bill continued to find issues with Johnny's decisions and bent over backwards to pick them apart. Not only did he strongly disagree with the Nickel Mines decision even after the lawyers ruled it legal, he disagreed with Johnny's decision that Leon Stoltzfus's move from manufacturing building to manufacturing building didn't warrant a hearing, despite the fact that it had also housed a fiberglass manufacturer. The ball started rolling that ended a week before Thanksgiving with Bill, now the head supervisor, requesting his resignation.

Johnny, so tired of the nitpicking and lack of common sense, called up his friend who ran the local golf course and got a job mowing grass there for the coming summer. At Thanksgiving he and Patti, in their new mini-van, drove most of the grandkids down to Audra's to eat the traditional meal and fill her in on everything that was happening in Bart. Audra felt safe to tell him a little secret that had driven her during the summer:

"Way back in April when you were getting ready to have your gallbladder removed," she confessed, "I had this thought—it just flashed across my mind—that you were going to die in December." She laughed at herself. He tried to laugh it off, too, but it stuck in the back of his mind.

Feeling home free now that with his consulting business he'd still be around the perpetual prayer service—though not as often, he assumed—he submitted his resignation. Johnny's former friend and engineer, Derrick Miller, took over as the Bart Township zoning officer. From then on anyone who wanted to build something in Bart had to pay triple what they had before and fill out the paperwork precisely, or his picky secretary would send it back, even if it was just a missing phone number that had been on all the other pages.

***

A few days into December after another round of complimentary golf with "the boys," he began to feel something new in his lungs, a dull pain he didn't recognize, unlike the chemo or the cancer from before. Just different. He assumed it was just the last of the Bad Guys dying off and decided to wait to tell his doctor about it at the next appointment over a month away. He didn't want to think about it and wasn't going to mention it to anyone; it would only cause worry and it was probably nothing.

But then he did mention it. He told his wife who texted Audra who called him, afraid her premonition really might come true after all, and pleaded with him to call the doctor.

"Yeah, but it's not like before. I mean, I feel great," he insisted. He couldn't help but think that submitting his resignation had something to do with it. Was the work that God had put him there to do, done?

He and the cancer center played phone tag back and forth—Johnny never getting the return call due to their poor cell reception in their basement apartment and the fact that he never answered his phone on the golf course. After the third round of leaving a message after hearing, "if this is an emergency..." with instructions about what to do next, he decided it wasn't an emergency and to wait. He didn't want to mess up Christmas for everyone.

When Audra arrived for the holiday he had her take a picture of him in front of his quilt that now hung proudly on his living room wall behind the TV. They went to the local drug store to print out a copy to give to Elsie who had been asking him for one since the party.

After dropping off the picture at the King's house (no one was home) the pair headed toward Dan's to shoot the breeze. "Oh, I just found out one of the stories I been telling for years isn't true," he confessed on the way. "You know the one about the kids running out of the schoolhouse because the angel told them to? I was talkin' to one of the fathers who had two kids shot, and he said that wasn't true."

Rounding the corner to Hometown Builders, they passed a familiar man standing in the drizzle on the sidewalk, wearing a fluorescent police poncho that looked extra odd when combined with a straw hat and a long beard.

"Was that Antique?" Audra asked. Johnny did the wave and point and said it was.

No one was in at Dan's office either, but the reason became clear as they heard the sirens scream from across the street.

"Wait. How did Dan and Antique know there was a fire?"

"Oh, they've all got the police scanners," he explained as they headed toward the next stop. "It's what they live for."

On the way back, Dan was in his office so they stopped to

chat. Happy to see his former party planning partner, he shook her hand with strength and pointed out the thank-you card she had sent him after the party that he pinned to his cork board on the wall. Johnny filled him in about the latest problem with the township and how everyone he came in contact with was unhappy with the exorbitant prices now charged for zoning. Dan shook his head and agreed, showing him the bill he received for the inspection services on the expansion project. "I tell ya," Johnny said, "I wish I hadn't-a stopped 'em. You woulda been done!"

Back in the apartment, Audra played Johnny the audio from the party of which he could only listen to seconds of before he had to turn it off or become a puddle. She broke the news that the book he had commissioned in February wasn't going to be all about the Amish, though his stories would be in there. An even better story had taken over: the story of his miraculous recovery from cancer. She read him the first two chapters, still rough drafts, and he smiled ear to ear the whole time, laughing at his own jokes as Audra recited them.

***

At his appointment for blood work the Wednesday before his three month check-up, two days before the new year, he was nervous. Audra's premonition still had time to come true. He could still drop dead like his father did.

He saw Dr. Caruso briefly and mentioned the new pain he'd been having, sure to include that he was "feelin' great," and "so much better than the year before, there's no contest." Just to be on the safe side, the doctor ordered another set of bone scans to be done on the 5th, the day before the next week when he'd be back for his next checkup and new PSA.

On New Year's Eve, Johnny called Audra who ran to her porch to answer, fearing the worst. "Hey little girl!" he said from his recliner. "I'm calling to test out this new contraption your brother gave me for Christmas so I can get calls in the basement!" He updated her about the reorganization meeting in Bart on Monday, the scans he was going for on Tuesday, and the doctor's appointment on Wednesday. Thursday was going to be the hearing for Dan and Abe. "Hey, I have, what, eight hours to go?" he said, happily.

"Huh?" Audra said, confused.

"I will have made it through December!" He laughed his big laugh.

The morning of the appointment was the first truly cold morning since the unusually mild winter began, and frost covered every windshield. From Ruth's house twenty minutes away, Audra called her father who hated for anyone to be late, to let him know she was running behind, maybe ten minutes past their rendezvous time, hoping he wouldn't be frantic. She hadn't expected to have to bust out the ice scraper. "Don't you worry. Take your time," he assured her calmly. "We have plenty of time."

He climbed up the brick pathway, desolate and white save for some lingering, tall decorative grasses, and soothed his own nerves by starting up the minivan and getting the heat going. He had decided that if the doctor said the cancer had come back already, he was going to quit golf, since he would need every ounce of strength his weary body could muster to fight the Bad Guys again—and he didn't know if he even could.

Audra pulled up, and he greeted her cheerily with an underlying hint of uncharacteristic stoicism. When Patti took the driver's seat, she backed out of the driveway, stopped in the cul-de-sac to make a three point turn, and looked in her rear view mirror at her husband's worried face. "How are you feeling?"

"I'm OK. Anxious," he admitted.

"I bet," she said and put the minivan into drive. "I was just telling Audra that you've been feeling so good that I don't think this will turn out to be anything."

It was true. Compared to how he felt at this same time last year, it was like night and day. From the middle of the first row of back seats, he confidently agreed with his wife, though his folded arms, furrowed brow, and subdued demeanor told a different story.

They arrived on time for them—early for everyone else—and signed in on the sheet in front of the sliding glass panes in the waiting room. For ten minutes they sat watching the clock until Paula took her position at 8:00 am.

"Hey Mr. C.!" she exclaimed with a big smile when she noticed him through the glass sitting in a chair next to his wife. "Howya been? Ya got any new Amish stories for me?"

Johnny told her he'd been feeling great and had a new Amish story every day. Just as he drew a big breath to begin, Dr. Caruso walked briskly through the door, his computer bag at the end of one arm, and hurried by to the medical offices, distracting his patient with a weird feeling of déjà vu. What would that doctor tell him in just a few minutes? Would there be another battle? Or were the Bad Guys just in their death throes? As the Coldirons waited to be called, Johnny rubbed his sweaty palms on his khaki cargo pants.

Finally a nurse stood at the door and called their name. His pulse quickened. She led them to their room and measured his vitals, remarking on his blood pressure; it was higher than last time.

"Well, I had about a pot of coffee this morning... and I'm pretty nervous," he confessed.

In the time between the nurse and the doctor, Johnny rambled on about his golfing buddies who had had their knees replaced and how much better they played afterward. "See, that's another thing. I'd like to get my knee fixed," he said, pointing to his right knee where the cartilage had been removed thirty years prior, "but that's depending on..." He didn't finish the sentence. There was no need.

"See, because when they did the scan, she stopped at my lungs where I've been feeling stuff, and she said, 'Wait, let me do that again,' and I just wonder if it's because she saw something there." Was this the bottom of the ninth?

When Dr. Caruso walked through the door all conversation came to an abrupt halt. Johnny prepared for the worst. Patti had already asked Brooke if she could move back in with her when he died. With so many people in the tiny room, Dr. Caruso had to place his computer on the patient table where Johnny wasn't seated this time. Though the seconds it took him to get situated seemed like hours, he got straight down to business as usual. They all held their breath.

"You're PSA is now down to 36," he stated to cheers all around. However, it was the report from the scans that would really let Johnny know if he should go for that new knee or not.

"And your CT scans," Dr. Caruso said, panning through his computer, then looking up at the worried faces, "which investigated the area you were concerned about," he confirmed with a nod and looked back to his screen to read, "treated with Lupron and chemo..."

"You and me, Doc," Johnny interrupted, nervously shaking his head, "we've gotta talk about that chemo."

The doctor smiled slightly. "No, no more chemo anytime soon. Nothing new," he assured his patient and returned to paraphrasing the report as if he were translating a foreign language. "The thing that they could see in the area around here before," he moved his arm he wasn't leaning on to indicate the rib cage, "they can't see at all anymore. It's completely gone."

Johnny hoped he really heard what he thought he heard but didn't want to celebrate just yet. Patti and Audra gasped in amazement.

"They don't see any lymph nodes in the back of your abdomen or any lymph nodes anywhere else. There's no evidence that they can actually see your prostate cancer."

All at once, like diving in a pool on a hot summer day, a refreshing relief flooded Johnny's chemo brain as he exhaled every bit of worry and anxiety he had collected over the past month in one enormous sigh. It was a miracle. He really was home free. He began to fantasize about all the golf he could play with a good knee. He might even get back to his former glory. In summary, there was no change in the bone scan and his labs "looked great."

"So what you're tellin' me, Doc, is," Johnny said and paused to catch the young medical professional in the eyes, "I should plan for the future?"

"I've been telling you that all along!" he snapped, with his eyebrows raised.

"Well, we started out in a bad condition..."

"We did, and we fixed that."

"Yeah, you did," Johnny said humbly, "and I-"

"No." The doctor cut off his patient and shook his head in serious disagreement. *"You did."*

"Well," Johnny chuckled and paused to reflect, "I had a lot of help."

They went on to talk about how the chemo had "kicked his ass" and how his golfing buddies tried to get him to play off the women's tees but that he refused because "that would take away some of my fight." The men chatted about their mutual love for America's favorite pastime and how an era of Phillies baseball had ended, and there would never be one like that again in their lifetimes.

Dr. Caruso said he'd see him again in another three months unless something new came up and told him where to go down the hall to get another dose of Lupron. While Patti and Audra wandered to the waiting room, Johnny gladly dropped his trousers for nurse Rhonda to administer his shot.

Pulling out of the parking lot, Patti's brow softened and her shoulders relaxed as she sighed, "That was a close one." Audra beamed. Meanwhile in the backseat, Johnny, like a kid who hit his first home run, rushed to report the good news of his new PSA number and that the cancer was "nowhere to be found," calling Ruth and Cheryl, and texting Huston the same thing. He asked Aileen to pass on to Frank that "he'll have to play golf with me a lot longer," and told her how nervous he had been and what a great day it was already.

After getting the word out to everyone else he could think of, he relayed to Patti and Audra a story from moments ago when he was in with the nurses, nearly bouncing out of his seat:

"So when I was just in there and the nurse was givin' me the shot, I was tellin' her what my PSA was down to now and how I'd been so nervous about this one because what I had been feelin.' And I told her, I says, 'Now they can't find any cancer at all.' She looked at my chart and saw where I started, and her eyes bug out real big and she says, 'Wow. That's amazing!' " he said and laughed a big triumphant laugh, throwing his head back to the mini-van's gray ceiling. "And then she looked at me and she goes, 'John,' she says, 'you are truly *remarkable*!' "

Johnny and his quilt

Afterword

As of this publication a year later, Johnny has made it past his sixty-fifth birthday, which his wife is calling his first. His PSA is down to an amazing 24 and continues to fall, though much, *much* more slowly than before. He complained about this fact to Dr. Caruso, who then gave him a little lecture that Johnny loves to retell.

Johnny and Patti moved out of Young John's basement and rent the little, yellow house on the corner that he had his eye on and that their daughter, Brooke, bought. His grandkids stay overnight regularly, and he still keeps his junk food paradise well stocked with goodies from his favorite Amish discount grocery store.

He now works exclusively as a building consultant to the Amish, busier than ever, and knows he needs to charge more, but can'. bring himself to raise his rates. Though a lifelong Republican, he defends Obama when the Amish talk him down because "if he didn't make it so I had to get insurance, I wouldn't be here."

Due to his arthritic knee, he hasn't been playing as much golf as before. However, he is considering a knee replacement but wants to pay for it completely out of his pocket like Antique did.

All in all things are going pretty well for The Amishland Storyteller and self-proclaimed "Roving Bishop." Remarkably well, actually.

Acknowledgments

There are many people who helped make this book happen, from assisting with the technical aspects of writing it, to lending photos and/or participating in the actual story. I am grateful for each of you.

First and foremost, I'd like to thank my father, Johnny Coldiron, for his stories and answering my zillion questions to things that I didn't record or forgot to write down and couldn't remember.

I'd also like to thank Dr. Michael Costello and the entire staff of Penn Medical Center who took such excellent care of my dad during that difficult time and continue to do so.

Now, in no particular order, I'd like to thank the following: Patti Coldiron, Val Keene, David and Kate Lapp, Professor Roger Gilles and his "Working with Manuscripts" class at Grand Valley State University, Gwenn Garland, Sonya Carmack, Pat Meusel, Don Singleton, Carrie Carmack, Holly Carmack, Vanessa Smullen, Debby Dowdy, Terry Tabb, Dave and Cheryl Huston, Frank and Aileen Parrish, Aaron and Anna Mary Esh, Amos Esh, Merv Fisher, John Richards Esh, Marvin Fisher, Antique, Ike and Catherine Lapp, Leon Lapp and family, Basia Manniso, Dolly Coldiron, Brenda Peterson, Ruth Coldiron, Randy Coldiron, Diane Cavender, Dr. Stephen "Nemo" Niemoeller, Tommy "Ho", Ronnie Grimm, Andy Jennison, John and Holly Coldiron and kids, Brooke and Joe Brown and kids, Jennifer Miller, and Adam and Catherine Kegley. Last but not least, I want to thank Mike, Quinn, and Irie Carmack for being so understanding about the time I spent on this project. I love you all.

28280413R00149

Made in the USA
Middletown, DE
20 December 2018